THE WINDMILLS AND
OF BEDFORD.

– past, present and future

HUGH HOWES

with the support of Bedfordshire County Council

Book
Castle
PUBLISHING

Published March 2009 by
Book Castle Publishing
2a Sycamore Business Park
Copt Hewick
North Yorkshire HG4 5DF

Reprinted May 2010

ISBN 978 1 903747 97 1

Typeset and designed by Caroline and Roger Hillier
The Old Chapel Graphic Design
www.theoldchapelivinghoe.com

Printed by DIRECT-POD, Brixworth, Northampton

front cover (clockwise from top left): Stevington Windmill *photo Adrian Fett*;
Stotford Mill *photo The Stotford Mill Preservation Trust*; Upper Dean Windmill in May 2008;
Bromham Mill *photo Adrian Fett*

previous page: Stevington Windmill in 1936
photo Fred Woodbridge, reproduced by kind permission of Marion Field

CONTENTS

AUTHOR'S PREFACE

I worked for the County Planning Department of Bedfordshire County Council from 1974 until 1989, for the most part on regional and strategic planning. However, I was also interested in the conservation and archaeological work of the Department. At the time the County Council was engaged in the *Survey of Bedfordshire* which was a study of the county's historic environment. It was to be published in sections and two volumes were produced, *Brickmaking* by Alan Cox and *The Roman Period* by Angela Simco.

A colleague showed me a collection of photos of windmills in the county taken by the late Harry Meyer of Letchworth during cycle tours in the 1920s and 1930s. From this came the idea of producing a companion book to the Survey of Bedfordshire which materialised as *Bedfordshire Mills* in 1983. I was introduced to the late Peter Dolman who loaned me the research he had completed when he was at Bedford Modern School. Peter's work was a major contribution to the understanding of the extent and distribution of windmills in the county and also their mechanical details. I am pleased to have been able to include some of Peter's hitherto unpublished drawings in this book.

The book was based extensively on the *Sites and Monuments Record* which was compiled and maintained in the County Planning Department. One very kind correspondent described my book thus:

It was, at the time, groundbreaking because it was the only complete record of mills, past and present, in Bedfordshire since Domesday Book.

Memories of everyday milling were dying fast when I started work on that book in the early 1980s. Corn milling in general and flour milling had started to decline before the First World War and had reached the point of virtual extinction by the 1960s. Nevertheless, I was able to interview a considerable number of people with direct experience of milling. As they are all no longer alive their spoken word has assumed an increased value in terms of immediacy. Since publication two further records of wind milling came to light. These interviews provided a flavour of what it was like to work in these local mills and provided a valuable record of oral history. They provided a supplement to the technical details in the Sites and Monuments Record and gave a historical and social context to *Bedfordshire Mills.* I have brought forward much of this material into this book.

I have seen the purpose of the present book as being a little different from the 1983 publication which was primarily intended as a comprehensive compilation of all the records on milling that were readily available. The current book *The Windmills and Watermills of Bedfordshire — past, present and future* is designed to provide an interpretative guide to what can be learned from the surviving mills. I have omitted most of the references to mills that disappeared long ago and substituted a chapter on the problems of restoration, conversion and after-use. I have also largely ignored mills that have been converted to houses, as in most cases the machinery has been removed. The loss of a mill's machinery robs it of much of its interest.

I am indebted to Adrian Fett, Stuart Antrobus, Paul Redwood and Ron Roper for all the help they gave me on the text of Chapter 3 and to Stephen Coleman, Historic Environment and Information Officer of Bedfordshire County Council. The staff of the Mills Section of the Society for the Protection of Ancient Buildings (SPAB), Simon Hudson, Ron Cookson and Luke Bonwick gave me much assistance. I am also grateful to the conservation officers of the District Councils for updating me on a number of individual cases. My thanks go to David and Bill Jordan for their help in providing information on their family business and to David Lindsey for updating me on the position of several mills in South Bedfordshire.

My thanks go also to Rachel Hodge, Mandy Bromwich, and Alan Harman for showing me around, respectively, Bellows, Barton, and Doolittle Mills. I am also grateful to Clifton Ibett for providing information on Milton Ernest Mill and for arranging access. Similarly John and Sarah Doonan helped me on Upper Dean Windmill and allowed me access.

I am indebted to Ed Burnett in particular and Bedfordshire County Council for its contribution which has enabled the inclusion of colour pictures.

Finally, I would also like to thank my wife, Monica, for reading the typescript, making many helpful suggestions, for working on the photographs and for ensuring that the text was in order.

In defining the technical terms used in each chapter I have drawn on *A Consolidated Glossary of British Mill Terms* compiled and edited by Tony Yoward and published by SPAB in 1996.

Contrasting styles of waterwheels. The massive double wheels at South Mills, Blunham (opposite, left) powered by a reliable source of power contrasts with the tall, narrow and overshot one at Barton (opposite, right) where a small stream powers a simple milling installation (*photos Beds CC photographic unit*). The wheel at Bromham (above *photo Beds CC collection donated by G.A. Anstee*), here seen in its manufacturer's yard, is a breastshot wheel using unenclosed buckets.

CHAPTER 1

The Story of Flour Milling in Bedfordshire

A flat county like Bedfordshire might not be regarded as favourable for the widespread use of water power. Furthermore the low rainfall in the east of England meant that streams were often small and their flows irregular. Yet this was the main cereal growing part of the country and, with the population of the country rising steadily until the Black Death of 1349, cereal production prospered as did these local mills. The sites of these water mills are very ancient. In the course of my researches I did not find any that had not been recorded in Domesday Book. Nevertheless, almost any stream can be dammed to provide a sufficient level of water to drive a mill if only for short periods. Using large wheels and lower gearing of the mill's machinery can enable the millstones to rotate at the right speed. Both overshot wheels, as at Stotfold, and breastshot wheels, as at Bromham, can be found in Bedfordshire. The former are more efficient in that they have buckets so that the weight of the water drives the wheel; breast shot wheels use the force of the water rather than its weight to drive it. (*See Note 1 for an explanation of the technical terms used in this chapter*)

Until we developed our almost insatiable demand for water with the consequent abstraction from both rivers and groundwater, rivers were wider, deeper and had more copious flows than they do today. So watermills could be found not only on the main rivers of the county, the Great Ouse, the Ivel, the Flit and the Ousel, but also on the minor tributaries whose volumes of water are now very meagre. The building of mills in such relatively unpromising locations, few of which have survived today, reflects very different economic circumstances from those which began to impinge from the 1850s onwards. The cost of transport in pre-industrial times put a premium on the local availability of milling facilities. However limited the source of power might be, it was less of a constraint than the poor communications systems. The proximity of a mill was of paramount importance for local farmers.

Between the river valleys lie substantial tracts of countryside with no accessible

A Straker-Squire steam lorry provides for local collection and delivery. It is at Kempston Mill in the early years of the 20th Century and shows a characteristic local registration number of the period. The driver was George Harris who won a gold watch for his feats in lifting the 20 stone sacks of flour as seen on the lorry. The owner of the mill, William Horn, is standing at the rear of the lorry.
photo supplied by John Clover

water power. They comprise the rolling countryside of north Bedfordshire and the western part of mid Bedfordshire and the Chiltern scarp slope. Windmills became common in these areas as Bedfordshire was early in using this new technological development. The watermills had enjoyed a monopoly position for grinding grain and everybody in the medieval village depended on the miller for their daily bread. His social position was paralleled by his economic position because the cost of having flour ground came third only to feudal dues and tithes. The advent of early windmills which could be set up on odd pieces of land outside the ownership of the Lords

Sundon post mill with sail cloths furled. It was moved to a site at Tebworth Road, Toddington, in 1847 where it survived until blown down in the 1880s. *County Record Office*

of the Manor started to offer some competition to the old medieval system just at a time when a growing population's need for ground meal was beginning to exceed the capacity of the water mills in medieval times (*Ref 1*).

The existence of a windmill at Leighton Buzzard was recorded by 1212 and further ones elsewhere in the 1220s and 1230s. They must have been amongst many built during the middle ages and known only from passing references in documents. They were mostly light, simple structures that could be easily erected, moved elsewhere or demolished, leaving little trace of their existence. These early post mills could be moved some distance away. One at Sundon was moved to Toddington in 1847 where it was placed on an old-established mill site. Similarly the post mill known as Flemmon's Mill stood on the Heath Road on Shenley Hill at Leighton Buzzard until 1860 when it was dismantled and re-erected at Whipsnade.

For milling, as with everything else, the outbreak of the Black Death in 1349 and the sudden fall in the population marked the end of a long period of growth and prosperity. The period of agricultural expansion was over, the population had been nearly halved and much cereal production ceased. The number of water and windmills operating must have fallen dramatically as arable land was turned over to pasture.

There are records of at least one hundred and forty windmills at one time or another but only Stevington has survived in a complete state. However, some eighteen others still existed well into the 20th century. Stevington represents the earliest type, the post mill. The body of the mill, often known as the buck, could be rotated around the post, enabling the miller to turn the whole mill so that its sails could catch the wind from whatever direction it might come. Other examples of this early type once stood at Bolnhurst, Lower Dean, Keysoe and Riseley.

The second, and later, type of windmill was the tower mill. This was a considerable improvement on the post mill in that the main body was a fixed

John Filsell of Keysoe Mill demonstrates how to turn a post mill to face the wind. Having raised the Thaltur to lift the steps off the ground he is seen pushing the tail pole so that the sails would face head on into the wind. *photo Rex Wailes 1936*

building and only the cap and sails turned to face the wind. Tower mills consisted of stone or brick cylindrical towers and often occupied sites where post mills had once stood. They had fantails, a device dating from about 1745 which automatically turned the sails into the wind. Often they had patent sails, invented by William Cubitt in the nineteenth century, a feature that that made the miller's life simpler, safer and more efficient. They replaced the common sail of the type that can still be seen at Stevington which had to be covered with canvas and reefed by hand to suit the varying winds. This was a laborious process that

Potton Tower Mill in 1926. *photo H. Meyer*

could not be carried out whilst the mill was running. Patent sails, in contrast, consisted of a row of spring mounted shutters which opened automatically if the wind became dangerously strong. They could also be controlled by a chain hanging out of the back of the windshaft, low enough for the miller to reach it from the ground.

The third and final evolution of the windmill was known as a smock mill because early examples clad in canvas were said to resemble a shepherd in his smock. They consisted of octagonal timber towers built on brick bases and were said to be of Flemish design. Essentially they were a cheaper version of the tower mill but usually enjoyed the sophistication of fantail and automatic patent sails. There were at least five smock mills in the county, at Flitwick, Great Barford, Henlow, Riseley and Biscot.

Biscot Smock Mill in 1935 in its final years. *photo H Meyer*

The period 1750–1850 is often described as the golden age of milling and most mills were substantially rebuilt during these hundred years to accommodate the latest industrial technology. There was a trend back from cattle farming towards arable in general and cereals in particular, reviving the demand for milling. In the last half of the eighteenth century many of the agricultural improvements associated with such famous names as Turnip Townsend and Robert Bakewell were taking place and milling technology made parallel advances. The windmills at Bolnhurst, Keysoe, Riseley and Stevington date from this time. So do most of the Upper Ouse watermills together with Hyde Mill on the Lea and the Flit mills at Flitwick, Maulden and Clophill. They were built in what industrial archaeologists call the rural vernacular tradition; in other words in a similar style to local barns and dwellings There are records showing that there were a total of 141 mills which ground corn in over 80 parishes in the county at that time. (*Ref 2*)

The late19th century, however, brought fundamental changes in the pattern of rural life and in particular the economics of flour production. In contrast to the 'golden age' of milling the hundred years after 1850 were characterised by decline, decay and destruction of the county's mills. These changes were to prove fatal for small scale milling by the local man. Initially the increase in grain stimulated production in the existing local mills. The Corn Laws in particular created the demand for home produced flour. They protected British farming, after the Napoleonic Wars, from foreign competition through import tariffs, and ensured high prices for the benefit of producers at the expense of the rapidly growing industrial cities. They were repealed in 1846. The twin results were firstly that cheaper imported grain, mainly from the United States and transported by steam ships and the rapidly developing railway network, was available to feed the new industrial centres, but secondly that lower prices made the position of British farmers, and in turn millers, ever more tenuous. The repeal of the Corn Laws effectively brought the golden age of milling to an end. But by the mid century the towns, first Luton and later Bedford, were attracting the rural

Flitwick Water Mill. The main structure, dating from the early 19th century, is timber framed and clad with horizontal weatherboarding and a prominent luccam or sack hoist. It is typical of the vernacular style of mill building from the 'golden age' of milling.

population and growing rapidly. There followed a rising demand for the bulk supply of flour to feed the increasingly urban population. The local mills simply could not meet this demand because of the limited flow of the county's rivers and the uncertainty of the wind. Many millers therefore improvised either by upgrading their equipment or by concentrating more on animal feeds and less on flour.

It is interesting to see how far millers were prepared to go in investing in these aids to milling. Some were clearly prepared to offer competition to the large scale industrial mills by upgrading their mills with the latest technology in order to get the most out of their existing mills. Others probably felt the times were against them and that such investment would offer little, if any, return.

The late Frank Hipwell (*Ref 3*), for example, recalled that the windmill at Sharnbrook was built:

> *To act as a standby or assistant to the Old Mill driven by the brook, in the hope that wind might be available when water was short. The juxtaposition of two such mills under the same ownership was not an unusual arrangement, giving the miller an alternative of two natural elements from which to draw power.*

But he also demonstrated the inherent inability of the old mills to respond to ever more pressing needs:

> *Water sometimes ran out before his grist, when the unfortunate customer had to wait a longer or shorter period, depending on the flow of the brook at the time, for the balance of his meal to be made. When this happened the wheel-gate was shut down until sufficient water had collected to allow operations to begin again. However time did not press a century ago.*

Time soon did begin to press and new measures were needed. Faced with this kind of competition local millers increasingly adapted their mills to be run by portable steam engines, traction engines and subsequently internal combustion engines or electric motors to overcome the problem of a reliable source of power, particularly at the critical harvest time of year when natural power was at its weakest. The inventory of a lease in 1907 of Barton Mill includes a reference to '4 ft iron drum with crank complete to connect steam engine to the machinery of the mill'.

There were mortal blows for both agriculture and, in turn, milling, between 1870 and 1880. A series of bad harvests in 1875, 1876 and 1877 made it increasingly difficult for small rural mills to meet urban needs.

Holme Mills in 1910, rebuilt as an 'industrial' mill, in contrast to its predecessor shown on page 92.
photo supplied by David Jordan

These seismic changes in the food supply caused the building of very large steam driven flour mills close to the ports. Importing American techniques of mass production and using roller crushers instead of stones and benefiting from a more constant source of power they were far more efficient than traditional local mills and better able to supply bulk white flour for the expanding towns and cities.

The mills in the Ivel valley successfully resisted the long decline for several years after most other mills in the county had succumbed. They were helped because the River Ivel enjoys a sustained and constant flow of water even in summer. Millers sought to move from breastshot wheels to overshot wheels by embanking the river above the mill to increase the fall at the mill site. Many of the mills were rebuilt in Victorian times in the industrial tradition. They are large and factory-like, mostly of four storeys, and are built of white or yellow gault brickwork with roofs of Welsh slate. They employed the latest technology: turbines sometimes taking the place of waterwheels and roller crushers substituting for stones. Turbines were installed during this period at Stoke Mills, Holme Mills and Bellows Mill. The public taste for white bread meant that stone ground flour was no longer popular. The new roller crushers were designed to produce white flour in large quantities and made traditional milling with stones almost obsolete. Henceforth grain was gradually reduced to flour by being repeatedly passed between pairs of rollers which revolved at different speeds. Break rolls are grooved rollers which separate the grain from the chaff. The second stage is performed by reduction rolls which mill the grain into flour.

Elevators were an improvement on the sack hoist. They consist of a belt with buckets attached. The grain, or meal or flour is scooped up by the buckets on the bottom floor and discharged on the top floor as the buckets are inverted. It may then be distributed by a screw auger which is used for transmitting grain and discharging it into any of the bins on the top floor selected by the miller.

I was lucky enough to have interviewed some millers who witnessed the changes during the early part of the 20th century. William Hipwell, for example, speaking in 1982 explained:

> Instead of crushing the grain these machines scooped the kernel out and at the same time they cleaned the inside of the skin, the spiral grooves varied between millers according to how fine or coarse a separation you wanted.

A further development was the plan sifter otherwise known as pendulum dressing machines or, more affectionately, 'drunken elephants'. Both Stoke Mills at Sharnbrook and Holme Mills at Biggleswade were equipped with them. In this way they were able to compete for several years with the great steam mills. The east of the county has always been a prosperous agricultural area, with soil of excellent quality fully exploited down the centuries, and grain provided plenty of business for local millers. Its well developed road, rail and waterway network furthermore ensured the survival of a milling industry long after decline had set in elsewhere. The Great North Road, the Great Northern Railway and the Ivel Navigation ensured that millers could benefit from cheap transport but they were also entitled to levy a toll of three pence per barge passing through the locks adjacent to their mills as a form of compensation for loss of water from their head races (Ref 4).

These technical developments rendered obsolete all the windmills and forced the watermills either to modernise or to go out of business. The combination of improved inland transport and long life flour took away the need for local production of flour. In the post-war years the remaining flour mills became involved in a commercial battle, inevitably to be lost, to the large baking companies. Speaking in the early 1980s William Hipwell recalled how Stoke Mills at Sharnbrook had been affected:

After the war the small bakers gradually disappeared and we found that we were selling flour to the big millers and it was an extremely expensive job and they could call the tune.

Essentially millers faced a deal with one of the big four, Ranks, Spillers, the Coop and Garfield Weston. Essentially the arrangement was that in return for compensation the machinery was scrapped or disabled and the mill silenced for ever. This was the fate of roller mills at, for example, Stoke Mills, Sharnbrook and Hyde Mill. Only Jordans resisted this deal and Holme Mills, as a result, has the only remaining set of roller mills in the county.

With a rare mixture of bonhomie and threat J. Arthur Rank summed up the position in a New Year message on 29 December 1954. Wishing the local millers 'a very happy and successful New Year' he sent out this message (or warning?):

This is the most crucial year in the history of milling because we shall either become bob-a-sack suckers or first class millers. And the simple fact is that it rests with ourselves, with no other person or circumstance. It is just as simple as this, play cricket and become a first class miller, or don't care a damn for anyone and become a sucker. In making your choice, remember the banana — when it leaves the bunch it gets skinned.

The last operating windmill in the county was at Keysoe. The late William Filsell was the brother of John the last miller of this post mill. They worked it from 1915 until the end of the Second World War. In 1975, at the age of 88, William remembered graphically why local milling disappeared (*Ref 5*):

We relied more or less on the little men, they would have an allotment, one part vegetables, a rood of wheat and a rood of barley for pigs. We used to do the grinding. My brother and me used to go round the villages and fetch it in from them and take it back when we had ground it. The government decided to subsidise farmers for wheat, oats and barley with tractors and harvesters. The subsidy was paid through

Keysoe post mill was built in about 1800. It was a typical early example of a post mill with a roundhouse. This was the last working windmill in Bedfordshire. By 1935 it was the only one where flour was still ground and dressed solely by windpower. Its roof was of the primitive straight pitched type (c.f. Stevington) and its body flared out at the bottom to form the roundhouse roof.
photo Rex Wailes

the big millers. So the little men had to go into the towns to find jobs. And when they packed up we lost business.

J Steele Elliott (*Ref 2*), writing in 1931 recorded the gradual loss of the county's windmills:

Upwards of 80 parishes in Bedfordshire have records of such mills in their history, whereas the present generation may not recall a tithe of them running. Biggleswade, Cranfield, Stevington and Keysoe remain and they are working but intermittently.

The others that are left are derelict and tempest shorn; in many instances they defy the elements by their wonderful construction of millwrights' workmanship and may serve a while for a few years longer as store-places for cattle.

In contrast to the county's watermills of whose heritage much still remains, very little has survived of the windmills whose revolving sails until the outbreak of the First World War must have been as common a sight as that of the parish church. Of the four windmills mentioned by Steele Elliot only Stevington has survived.

Prior to the 1914–18 Great War and for many years after, it was the custom that, following the harvesting of cereals, the villagers were allowed to "glean" the fields by picking up the heads of corn once the harvesting had been completed and the field raked. One " stook" of corn was left in the field denoting that it was not yet available for gleaning, but once this was removed, the public were at liberty to go into the field to pick up whatever ears of corn had been left behind. These gleanings were taken to the miller, where the corn was thrashed out and the wheat, beans or barley ground into flour which helped provide additional food for the winter months. (Ref 6)

By the 1940s and 1950s most windmills were greatly decayed. The next few years saw losses at an alarming rate. A typical tale of decay is that of the tower mill at Upper Dean. It ceased working in 1906. By 1931 when Steele Elliot's survey was published, it had lost two sails. By 1967 only two broken stocks were hanging on the pole end. The brake wheel was still in place but the ogee cap had gone. Without its protection the elements wrought havoc in the exposed machinery. Happily the cap has now been replaced and the structure is weather tight again.

Harnessing the wind has always been hazardous; there tends to be too much of it or too little. Windmills were exceptionally vulnerable to storm damage, and the mill left to decline in peace, like Upper Dean, is the exception. Most have met violent ends. They could for instance catch fire in high winds. If the wind caught the sails before the brake could be applied they would revolve with a force that could not be controlled by the brake. This is what happened to the post mill at Yielden which was burned down in a gale in 1877. The sails were forced into action and the friction from the brake set it on fire. Steele Elliot recounts:

The miller being helpless it was burned out. The sails continued to revolve in the holocaust until the whole collapsed.

Similarly Ben Anstee recalled that a storm had finished the working life of Cranfield Mill:

I was working as a boy of 11 that day in 1935 when the mill got out of control in a storm . It has never been worked since.

The mill was demolished in 1966 as the roof had shifted and the owners felt its condition had become unsafe. The tower itself was sound and proved hard to break up.

If a mill could be destroyed by a headwind, as just recounted, a wind from the rear could be even more damaging. The structure of the mill was designed to cope with a wind from the front. But if the sails were forced forward by a tailwind there were no bearings to hold the windshaft in place. The destruction of Keysoe Post Mill, the last working mill in the county, is recorded in the 1948 annual report of the Society for the Protection of Ancient Buildings:

Since 1943 this mill has changed hands several times and again this year it was offered for sale. As the Society was making enquires by telephone, news came through that it had been tail winded and blown down. Mr Rex Wailes visited and inspected the mill and found the structure, although broken beyond repair, was sound enough and the accident would not have taken place had the mill been in the hands of a working miller who would have kept the mill turned to the wind or had the shutters removed from the spring sails. Keysoe was the only mill in England where the flour could be ground and dressed solely by wind power and it is particularly regrettable that this unique example should have been destroyed owing to lack of proper precautions.

If Keysoe Mill was destroyed by a human failure to turn the mill into the wind, Potton tower mill was destroyed by an unusual mechanical failure. Normally a tower mill equipped with a fantail will turn itself into the wind automatically. However:

In the end of December 1927 a north-easterly wind had turned the cap to face in that direction and then calmed off leaving it in that position. On January 6th 1928, by one of those ugly whims of nature that every windmiller knows so well, a terrific south westerly gale came up and the wind vane , apparently frozen solid, would not move. Within a few hours the vane and sails were shattered almost beyond repair. It was not deemed economical to replace them as by that time the bulk of the milling trade was going to the great steam mills springing up about the county;

Cranfield tower mill was built in the late 1840s. Seen here in its prime it had four patent sails which drove three pairs of stones and flour dressers. It worked until 1935 when one sail was wrecked in a gale. It was built of red brick with a cemented finish. It stood about 55 feet to the acorn finial on top of its broad ogee cap. Around the base of the cap was a scalloped petticoat which stopped rain from getting in. The millstones were two pairs of Peaks and one of French burrs. The four double-shuttered patent sails of about 65 feet span are believed to have come from Houghton Conquest Mill in 1910. The original ones were much larger with a span of 70 ft.

so Potton windmill, once a pride of Bedfordshire, soon became derelict, another tombstone to a dead industry. It was finally demolished in 1955, leaving the tower half its original height.(Ref 7)

To end on a happier note, a niche market for wholemeal flour is growing. This has tended to favour small scale milling. Modern nutritional theory has shown the error of removing the bran rather than grinding wholemeal. Bran is still known as offals or leftovers, yet it contains the roughage vital to health. There is a growing interest in healthier lifestyles and the advantages of dietary regimes where the energy release is gradual and long lasting. An important element is avoiding the over-processing of the ingredients. The glycaemic index ranks carbohydrate concentrations in terms of their effect on blood glucose levels and has become fundamental to physical training. It enables athletes in particular and those interested in fitness to increase energy, lose fat and improve the general sense of well being. Roller mills, whatever their technical virtues, operate at such speed (up to 600 rpm) that they generate heat which kills off the enzymes. When I interviewed him in 1982 John Jordan explained that the more the process is slowed down the higher the nutritional value of the product:

> From about 1850 the bakers very misguidedly thought that if bread did not rise it was a slur on their ability to make bread. The presence of bran impaired the baking quality, so many millers introduced roller mills and threw out the bran for animal feed. But the big advantage of stone-ground flour is that it is full of enzymes. Making white flour means giving the humans all the starch and rubbish and the animals all the vitamin and protein. The big advantage of stone-ground flour is that it is cooler ground and is full of enzymes. We are trying to emulate stone-ground flour and have slowed our rollers down to 200rpm.

Just across the county boundary at Redbournbury Mill the James family conduct a model operation of food from field to table. The mill produces organic wholemeal bread from a variety of wholemeal flours. These are sourced locally and baked on site. There are two pairs of French burr stones which turn at 120 rpm. Justin James explains:

> We carefully monitor heat build-up as this can damage the flour. Some heat is beneficial as it helps natural oils in the flour to distribute, improving the baking and eating qualities of the flour.

There is an external overshot water wheel approximately 11 feet in diameter and about 8 feet wide. A low flow alleviation scheme for the River Ver by the Environment Agency has restored the flow with environmental benefits but there is rarely enough water to turn the wheel. The levels of water abstraction from aquifers to supply housing development is a significant issue for those seeking to revive water mills. Ironically the river level below the mill has risen in recent years giving rise to the additional problem of potential backwatering.

So flour in being produced not only at Bromham and Stotfold but also, just outside the county, at Redbournbury in Hertfordshire and Ford End Mill in Buckinghamshire.

Redbournbury Mill.

Conclusion

Of the 400 mills in Bedfordshire that were operational and making flour 150 years ago few remain. We are, however, fortunate to have three mills – two water mills and one windmill – preserved for posterity and open to the public. And it is now possible to see the process of making flour taking place at both Bromham and Stotfold watermills. Chapter 3 provides a detailed guide to these three mills and explains the processes by which flour was produced down the centuries.

References

1 Kealey, Edward J., 1987, Harvesting the Air, *University of California Press*

2 Steele, Elliot J., 1931, *Bedfordshire Historical Records Society* Vol XIV

3 Hipwell, F., 1949, 'The Mills of Sharnbrook', *The Sharnbrook Review*

4 Evans, M.C., 'A Brief History of the River Ivel', *Lock Gate* Volume 1

5 Tape recording made by the pupils of Lincroft School, Oakley, 1975

6 Written information supplied by E.M. Sharman dated 28th November 1984

7 Woodbridge, F., 1963, 'Potton Windmill', *Bedfordshire Magazine* Vol 9

Technical terms used in Chapter 1

• Power is transmitted from the waterwheel or windmill sails by a series of gears. In a watermill the wheel is mounted on an axle as is the **vertical bevelled pit wheel** which meshes with the horizontal **wallower** which drives a vertical shaft. This drives **the great spur wheel** to which the cogs, known as **stone nuts**, may be engaged to drive the **millstones**. The windmill works on a similar principle except that the upright shaft is driven from above instead of below.

• **Waterwheels** extract energy from water as it passes from a higher level to a lower level. An **undershot** wheel is driven by the impulse of water striking the lowest paddles. A **breastshot** wheel is turned by the weight of water in its buckets. An **overshot** wheel is where water is fed to the top of the wheel, discharging into buckets on the far side using the weight of water to turn it.

• **Turbine** A more efficient way of extracting energy from water using an enclosed impeller.

• **Post Mill** The earliest form of windmill where the timber body containing the machinery and carrying the sails is turned into the wind about an upright post.

• **Tower Mill** A windmill with a fixed masonry or brick tower with a revolving cap which carries the sails.

• **Smock Mill** A timber variant of a tower mill.

• **Sack hoist** A chain or rope mechanism for hoisting sacks to the bin floor. An **elevator** does the same thing by means of an endless belt with buckets or cups on it.

• **Tail Pole** A spar projecting from the rear of a post mill for turning the mill to face the wind.

• **Talthur** The lever pivoted on the side of the tail pole used to raise the ladder clear of the ground.

CHAPTER 2

The Miller at Work

The men who worked these mills required a wide range of skills and considerable powers of concentration. Eternal vigilance was the key to successful milling. Working the complex and specialised machinery of a mill was a skilled and potentially dangerous occupation at the mercy of either wind or water. The milling process essentially had four stages (*Ref 1*):

1. On arrival at the mill, the grain would be hoisted to the top floor in sacks whereupon it would be discharged into large storage bins.
2. From here, the grain would be fed through cleaning machinery before being hoisted once again to the bin floor.
3. It would then pass downwards through the millstones to emerge as meal from a spout on the ground floor.
4. Finally, the ground meal would be raised to bin floor level and passed through the dressing (sieving) machines to separate the different grades of flour.

Edrop Joseph Sharman was the last miller at Bolnhurst Windmill. His son provided this graphic account of his father working the mill: (*Ref 2*)

I well remember the action required to start the mill. My father first unfurled the cloth on the two sails, tied it back to the framework of each sail, then adjusted the shutters on the remaining two sails into the closed position. Following this he faced the sails into the prevailing wind, released the braking mechanism, adjusted the control of the millstone to be used, and the sails would then commence turning.

Being a post mill, the whole structure above the brick roundhouse had to be turned to face into the wind; this was done by the miller pushing on a tailpole using a yoke through which he put his head and shoulders, first having raised the mounting steps.

The cereals to be ground were raised to the top of the mill via a chain hoist which passed through the trap doors to the two floors. It was then fed into a bin through a chute to a hopper above the grinding stones, where it passed through a slipper into the eye of the stone and ground between the top stone, passing from there through a chute to the ground floor where it was bagged.

I recall the massive brake wheel attached to the main shaft and sails. Heavy steel weights were attached by rope to this braking mechanism which was brought into

The only known photograph of Bolnhurst
Windmill. *photo The Mills Archive*

use when the mill was not working. The
sails were unfurled and turned away
from the prevailing wind. The stones
themselves provided a great braking
effect when they were stationary.
Consequently, when the top stone was
raised for maintenance the braking
effect was very much reduced and it
was very important that the sails were
kept "out of the wind" and the brake
was made fully secure.

A detailed account of the working
of Duloe Windmill has been provided
by the late Dr F.L.Patterson (*Ref 3*)
who bought the mill in 1933 and
subsequently converted it into a house
immediately after the Second World
War. He provides a graphic account
of the machinery, even though it will
upset the molinological puritan to
read that one of the hoppers on the stones had been converted into a cosmetics
cabinet! The site is now in Cambridgeshire but was formerly in Bedfordshire.
This was a tower mill, a structure of much greater sophistication than the post
mills at Bolnhurst and indeed Stevington. Writing in 1953 he first provides a
technical description of how to operate patent sails which provided a greatly
superior method of trimming the sails to the wind than the tail pole and yoke
method described above.

*The fantail balcony was built on the ends of the two large projection pieces of
timber, known as the "sheers", which emerged from under the edge of the cone roof.
The purpose of the fantail sail was to keep the main mill sails headed into the wind.
If the wind veered to one side, the main sails would almost cease turning but the
wind could then strike the fantail which began to spin and, by a system of gearing,
would turn the whole cone on a circular cog track, just inside the edge of the roof,
until the main sails were turned into the wind again, and the small fantail sails,
being once more in shelter and edgeways to the wind, would then stop turning.*

*Hanging near the entrance door and suspending from the summit was a long,
light, strong chain. A pull on this would drag down an immense hook of cast-iron*

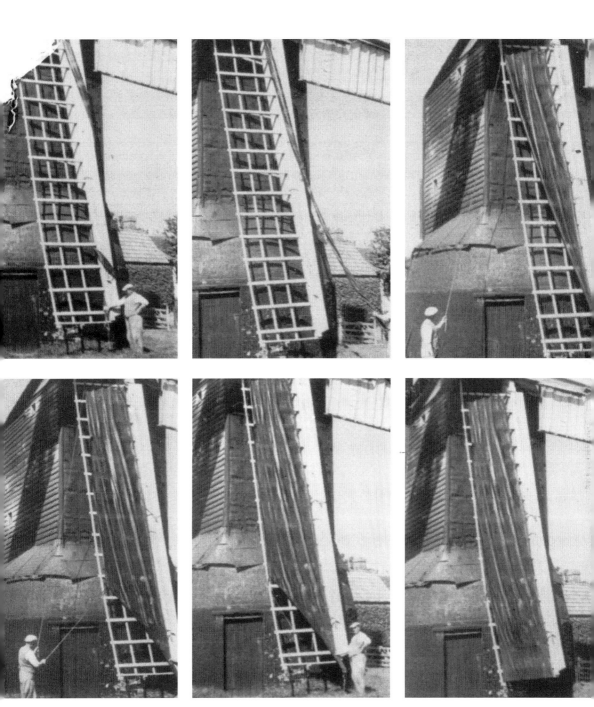

The late John Filsell demonstrates how to furl a cloth sail at Keysoe Mill. *photos R Wailes, 1936*

projecting from the fantail balcony, which was often at this side as the prevalent wind came from the south west. This hook, when thus depressed, would, within the cone-like roof, lever a long metal rod, as thick as the base of a man's thumb, straight through the centre of the trimmed elm trunk which formed the windshaft, and so out for 6 inches or more on the other side in the centre of the cross formed by the sails. Here this rod ended in a spider-cross of iron, the four bent ends of which were fastened by short connecting rods to four right-angled triangles of metal. These triangles, which were suspended, loosely from their right angles, on strong iron supports fastened to the great wooden arms of the sails, had long metal rods fixed to their next largest angles at the points of these (again jointed), so that, as the spider went in and out, the rods went perforce, to and fro, along the centre length of the wooden sails. These rods bifurcated, at a point a little less than half-way along the sails, and were then affixed to two long narrow strips of strong wood to which all the Venetian-blind like shutters were loosely jointed along the whole length of the lower edge of each of the single clockwise moving sails. Consequently, of course, the pulling of the afore-mentioned chain resulted in the opening and shutting of the shutters, for the iron hook to which the chain was fastened could be pulled both up and down, by dint of a single pulley system above it, over which part of the chain bifurcated.

This is a fascinating insight into the working of the most sophisticated type of windmill. It is a great shame that no examples of such mechanisms have survived in the county. Dr Patterson then describes the power train from the sails to the stones:

The giant brake wheel is fitted with replaceable cogs made of some hard wood, usually apple or hornbeam, and, for better wear, wooden cogs were usually made to engage with iron ones, in the case of the brake wheel with the iron wallower, as it is always called, a horizontal cogwheel, now resting on the floor of the cone, although, in its working days, it used to be some four feet above it. This wallower is fitted firmly in the usual way, by wedges, to the squared top of a "tree" of American pitch pine, which ran right down through the top two rooms of the mill, to turn the giant spur-wheel in the third room down, and this spur-wheel, a great iron cogwheel (with wooden replaceable cogs), turned three stone-nuts (or small cogwheels) which actually, through squared iron shafts (about 4"sq) turned the top mill stones of the three pairs of stones that were once in this room; one pair is still there but has been pushed back into a window (the south) embrasure, and the hopper over it made into a cosmetics cabinet!

He is describing the standard pattern of mill machinery. All the elements described above can be seen in the surviving mills. He then moves on to describe the sack hoist:

The tower mill at Duloe Hill was built in 1815 to replace a post mill. It last worked in 1916. Here it is in 1936 before conversion to a house in the late 1940s when all the machinery was removed.
photo H Meyer

Under the wallower a round wooden wheel about two feet in diameter (still in the cone) could be caused to engage with the wider surface of the wallower (and thus of course to be set spinning and winding the hoist higher) by pulling a rope, from the ground floor, that would hold this wheel up by means of a pulley fixed to the sheer. This was the sack hoist, by means of which the miller could hoist sacks of grain to the upper floors of the mill through the series of open trap-doors that ran up inside the west side of the mill to the upper floors of the edifice, using wind power for an otherwise heavy and arduous task. This sack-hoist wheel has a ribbed projection from it over which the rope went, and a twin ribbed roller as well, parallel to it, to give extra power of hoist (this is also still in the cone).

Dr Patterson then describes how the grain was fed through the mill:

Beneath the cone, the top room of the mill carried only the great turning squared shaft of American pitch pine and the sacks of grain, hoisted up there, and waiting to be spilled down square box-like shoots or "spouts" of wood to the lower floor where the actual grinding took place. These shutes were about 8" square and zigzagged down from floor to floor – a square wooden bin, narrowing to its base, resting on each floor to receive the ends of the shute, and collect the grain, before further transmission. The top two floors were then used for stacking the grain and transmitting it to the grinding room on the first floor ...When the grain was ground on the first floor it would pass out to the edges of these grooves and be collected under the wooden casing which covered the stones. From there it passed through a hole under the casing at one side and at the foot of it, and ran through a wooden spout to the ground floor where it emptied into bags hung up to receive it, on hooks against the wall. As these filled up they were replaced by the miller who had, naturally, to keep an eye on them. On the first or grinding floor, the grain arrived by spouts from the floor above, where the miller would spill it down these shoots and would enter first a long hopper, narrowing to its base, through which it would pass into a wooden "shoe", kept shaking by a spring drawing it against the square-edged, turning quant, which was cast in one piece with the stone-nut above (i.e. the cog in opposition with the great spurwheel). From this shoe it would be shaken into the hole in the centre of the stones and so out, sideways, to be ground into the grooves of the stones.

left: The miller is adjusting the tentering wheel that controls the gap between runner and bedstone and makes the flour finer or coarser. His left hand is in the flow of flour from the spout, judging its quality. Above the tentering wheel is a smaller thumbwheel. This controls the crook string which in turn adjusts the angle of the slipper. This adjustment regulates the speed at which the grain enters the millstones and affects the fineness of the flour but is itself determined by the speed of the millstones (more rpm, greater feed rate). The skill of the miller is in balancing the feed rate of the grain, the speed of the millstones, and the fineness of the flour.
photo Justin James

right: A hopper full of wheat.
photo Justin James of Redbournbury Mill

Finally he describes the milling process itself:

The third room down (or first floor up) or grinding floor. The great spur wheel, of cast iron, can be seen in the roof and has replacement wooden cogs itself which geared with the cast iron stone nuts. The stone nuts had a thick pitchfork-like end which linked over a metal "U" embedded across the hole in the centre of the top millstone so turning the stone.....On the top of their cover can be seen the sockets for the horse, a wooden framework that supported a hopper, or wooden receiving-bin for the corn to be ground ...a block of wood with a spike on it on which pivoted the wooden shoe kept shaking by knocking against the turning square edges quant (ie the shaft of the stone-nut), this being done by pulling it.

In the ground floor room was a pair of governors – cast iron balls a little bigger than a grapefruit, which operate a regulating device. As the mill went faster, the two heavy iron balls of the governors were spun faster. The tentering device, so-called, worked like a see-saw, and lowered the top stone when at speed to counteract centrifugal force which lifted it up....and was really mainly to ensure that the grain was ground smoothly and finely whatever the state of the wind at the time.

From the above it is clear that the millstones were at the heart of the mill. Even people who know nothing about how a mill works have probably seen a millstone at some time, perhaps used decoratively as a door step. They are generally about four feet in diameter, blue/grey in colour, with a pattern of grooves on their running surfaces and with a hole in the middle. They operate in pairs with a lower static bedstone and an upper revolving runner stone. They are a subject of study almost on their own and there are many subtleties which may elude the casual observer. The two main types of stone are represented in Bedfordshire. Monolithic stones of Derbyshire millstone grit are suitable for the coarse grinding of coarse grain, such as barley, beans, 'offals' or animal food. It is possible to mill perfectly good flour on well dressed Derbyshire peaks but they are not as good as French burrs for really fine flour. The latter are more suitable for producing the finer kinds of flour. Traditionally they come from the Marne Valley. However, they are no longer made there and the most practical option is a substitute obtainable in Holland. They were much more expensive; £36 brought a pair of French burrs in Victorian times with only £5 for a pair of Derbyshire peaks. Today, for comparison, a pair of French stones would cost between £3,000 and £5,000. They consisted of many pieces of hard quartz, held together with plaster of Paris and bound with iron hoops to ensure that the runner did not fly apart from centrifugal force. The pieces were imported from France and made up by specialist firms traditionally concentrated in Mark Lane in the City of London where the factors of machinery and millstones would receive their orders from the millers. One of the best known of these companies was *Millwright-Corcoram Manufacturing, Mark Lane, London*. Other such companies in Mark Lane specialised in other milling equipment such as bushel weighers and corn measures.

The stones were encased in wooden vats whose primary purpose was to prevent the flour flying about when it emerged around the circumference of the stones. Several good examples of complete vatted stones with hoppers and shoes still exist in the county. As explained by Dr Patterson the grain was fed into the centre, or eye, of the runner stone from a hopper in which it was stored above the stones. The miller could control the rate of flow by adjusting the angle of the shoe or channel along which the grain flowed to the stones. The adjustment was carried out with a crook string which ran over a pulley down to the floor below where the miller would normally be. A bell warned when the supply of grain was running low.

Furrows were cut from the eye (centre) to skirt (circumference) of both upper and lower stones and formed the cutting edge. This was a comparatively easy task. The skilled part of stone dressing lies in stitching or fluting French stones with a mill bill and thrift and in getting the working surface exactly flat and even. The tool itself was known as a bill and its wooden handle was called a thrift. The dress had to be renewed from time to time by the miller as the stones wore away. Far harder and more painstaking work was needed on the burrs than on the peaks. The stitching consisted of fine parallel grooves along the grinding surface or 'land' and served to grind the flour. Grains would be caught in the furrows and squeezed and rolled open; the stitches then scraped the flour off the bran and ground it. Mr Sharman of Bolnhurst recalled:

Every few months the top stone had to be raised by a chain and hoist, turned over and the surface of both stones "hand dressed" with a sharp steel bill secured in

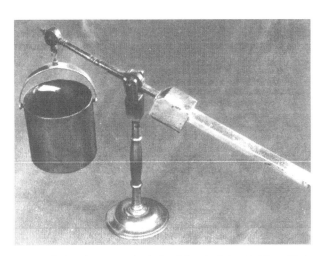

A chondrometer or bushel weigher. A vital part of the miller's equipment used for measuring the specific gravity of flour. It takes to pieces and fits in a small mahogany case for easy carriage. *photo C.W. Howes*

Stone furniture is a collective term for the wooden equipment which sits around and above the millstones. It includes the **vat** or **tun** which is a removable circular casing surrounding the stones and which contains the newly ground flour which flies out from between the stones. The **horse** is the frame supporting the **hopper**, into which the grain for milling is fed, and the **shoe** which is the inclined tapering wooden trough which feeds the grain from the hopper into the **eye** of the **runner** stone. The **damsel** agitates the shoe, thus feeding the grain at a constant rate into the eye of the stone. There may also be an **alarm bell** which is a warning device triggered by lack of grain in the hopper. These two installations are at Hyde End Mill. Also to be seen are the crown wheel and belt drive for powering auxiliary machinery. *photo Luke Bonwick*

Mary Quenby keeping Bromham Mill going while many men were away during the First World War. *photo supplied by Bedfordshire and Luton Archive Service*

a wooden thrift. I can well remember my father lying on a small sack of bran on the surface of the stone chip-chip-chipping away by candle light to sharpen the cutting edges of the stones and deepen the grooves through which the meal was released.

Dressing the stone was a skilled and labour-intensive business and was sometimes contracted out. John Clover of Kempston Mill explained:

You would have to dress the stones probably once a month; peripatetic craftsmen used to make a living from it. First they used to get a staff that was absolutely true, then they would make up some riddle (red lead) which would show up the high spots and then flatten them. Then they used to cut so many grooves to the inch. You lay across the stone with a sack of bran under your elbow and then chip...chip...chip... If you rubbed your finger over them one way you felt a sharp edge ...the other way you didn't.

It was vital to the safety of the mill that the stones should be level and properly balanced. Each stone weighed 15 cwt and turned most efficiently at speeds between 125 and 150 revolutions per minute. The actual clearance required very fine adjustment. Maladjustment could mean sparks flying, with a serious risk of fire. Tentering gear is the mechanism for adjusting the gap between the millstones, thus regulating the fineness of the meal. It may include a governor, which is a regulator generally of a centrifugal type to adjust the gap between the stones and ensure a constant quality of the product. They can be seen at both Stevington and Stotfold.

John Clover demonstrates how to 'stitch' or 'flute' a millstone using a mill bill and thrift. The skilled part of stone dressing lies in getting the working surface exactly flat and making a series of fine parallel grooves which serve to grind the flour. Grains travel down the furrows and, when caught, are squeezed and rolled open before being ground in the 'stitches'. The sectional construction of a French burr stone is clearly shown. *photo Beds CC Photographic Unit*

The control centre; the miller's office at Hyde End Mill where, from the window, he could keep an eye on the activities in the mill yard. *photo Luke Bonwick*

The minute particles of steel from the cutting tool became embedded in the skin of the millwright. This was the testimonial of their experience, and millers would ask them to show their metal before contracting them to work at his mill.

The miller was also said to have a 'golden thumb'. He was as subject to human frailty as anyone else. He might for instance keep his thumb inside the measure and thus retain a portion for himself. Or he would sweep out flour from the vats around the stones only after the customer had departed. Dishonesty can never have been so blatant as at Willington Watermill (*Ref 4*) where the last miller's wife took a basin of flour for her pudding from every load of corn ground in the mill. In any event the unfortunate customer could return home with less material than he had brought.

The work was hard and hazardous. Although almost all mills had sack hoists it was not always possible to use them, particularly during calm August harvest days when there was no wind or water power to spare. A sack of flour weighed 280 lbs (130 kilos). When Robert Prew was the miller at Sharnbrook one of his sons was killed falling from a ladder in the windmill while carrying up a sackful of beans.

The three mills that are open to the public and in working order represent the state of the art of milling at different periods (*see Chapter 3*). There were subsequent developments, notably in the more industrial mills in the Ivel valley and at Stoke Mills, Sharnbrook. These included turbines in place of waterwheels, and roller mills instead of millstones. Many were the injuries, often fatal, suffered by millers in days gone by. The miller certainly had to be quick witted for he had to face personal risks of this nature every day of his life. He worked in cramped quarters, close to machinery that lacked the safeguards which would be considered essential to any modern factory. There must have been temptations to work on the machinery without stopping it first. The local press in 1920 records an 'Alarming Accident at Duloe Mill':

Mr Albert James Green of Duloe Mill, Eaton Socon met with a very serious accident whilst at work about noon on Friday. He was in the act of adjusting or altering a screw in the lower part of one of his steam grinding machines – the machinery being in motion at the time – when one of his coat sleeves caught in the machinery and Mr Green was pulled into the wheels. Nearly the whole of his clothing was torn off him, even one of his leather gaiters being torn off his leg. Fortunately, the jam in the machinery threw it out of motion, but not before he had been badly knocked about. He was alone in the mill at the time but his cries for help attracted the attention of Mr Tom Farrer of Staploe who was near the mill. Mr

It was virtually impossible to lift an 18- or 20-stone sack from the ground. This self lifting sack barrow enabled sacks to be cranked up to shoulder height. *photo Beds CC Photographic Unit*

Farrer rushed into the mill and from instructions given by Mr Green was able to release him.

At first it was feared that Mr Green had several bones broken, but we are very pleased to say the doctor's examination proved that no bones were broken, and there were no internal troubles. The injuries include severe lacerations of the body – a very large piece of flesh being torn out of one part of his body; bruises; loss of blood and shock.

Happily he recovered sufficiently to live another 37 years. However, accidents of this kind demonstrated all too clearly the need for health and safety legislation.

The use of auxiliary steam engines imposed their own potential dangers. Ben Anstee of Cranfield recalled a horrific incident during one busy August harvest period:

We've been there till midnight. I would come home from school and if the wind weren't blowing we had to start the steam mill up. We had a lot to do. That was the idea (of the steam mill) so that we could work in all weathers. I remember the old steam mill exploding and scalding my Dad and that is how I came to use the windmill. The steam mill used to get white hot and you had to walk past to start and stop it. My Dad was going by and it burst and scalded him.

If lack of wind power could be a problem for windmillers, the variability of river flows could present another set of problems for a watermiller. He needed a plentiful supply of water in the reach above his mill to drive his water wheel. But he also needed to get rid of the water below his mill. If water backed up below the waterwheel, the power of the mill was considerably reduced. The minutes of Hipwell and Son record that the heavy floods in the winter of 1960/61 which raised the level of the Ouse below Stoke Mills, Sharnbrook, prevented the turbine from acting properly. And ice could bring the mill to a halt. One miller's headwater was the next miller's tail race. Water shortages could also be a problem: John Goodman, the eighth generation of the family to run Flitwick Mill, recalled:

If you had a very dry summer you could only be grinding for an hour in the morning and an hour in the afternoon because of the low supply of water.

This could result in disputes especially where water mills were closely spaced as on the Ivel. In a long-running feud between William Jordan and Henry Franklin (who owned both Biggleswade Mills and Langford Mills, the mills immediately respectively downstream and upstream of Jordan's Holme Mills) backwatering became a critical issue. John Jordan explained:

> We were responsible for the banks of the river between here (Holme Mills) and Henry Franklin's mill at Langford (the next mill upstream of Holme Mills). So what the old man did was to get all his men to raise the banks so that Henry Franklin had got a high tail water which would deprive him of power. Then Henry Franklin would send blokes along to knock a hole in the bank! Henry Franklin bought Langford Mill, they say, solely for the purpose of flooding William Jordan out.
>
> You would think they were very friendly but they weren't. If Henry Franklin sold flour for 5/2d a sack, William Jordan would do it for 5/1d and then Franklin would undercut him again. And it got worse than that. When there was a lot of rain the old man would get his butler, a fellow called Pedder, and say 'Go down the river and tell me when Mr Franklin puts his light out'. Pedder would come back at 11.00 at night and say. 'Henry Franklin has got his light out'. So my grandfather would say. 'Right Pedder open the sluices; we'll flood old Henry Franklin out!' They really had some fun in those days!

References

1 Bonwick, L., 2007, Hyde Watermill, East Hyde, *Hertfordshire/Bedfordshire Archaeological Building Survey Report* BMHC

2 Written information supplied by E.M. Sharman dated 28th November 1984

3 Typescript from photograph album of Dr F.L. Patterson loaned by Mrs Patterson March 1984

4 Godber, J., 1955, 'Willington', *Bedfordshire Magazine* Vol 5 1955

Technical terms used in Chapter 2

• **Brake wheel** The primary gear wheel in a windmill having a braking mechanism and mounted on a windshaft and having a bevel gear to drive the **wallower** which is the horizontal gear wheel which turns the vertical upright shaft.

• **Sails-common and patent** Sails are attached to **stocks** which drive the windshaft. They are either simple frameworks to which cloths are attached to catch the wind or patent sails which are shuttered, self regulating sails designed to achieve a constant speed irrespective of the force of the wind.

• **Fantail** A mechanism for automatically facing the sails into the wind consisting of a circular bladed fan mounted at the rear of a windmill and set at right angles to the sails.

• **Sheers** The principal timbers carrying the fantail.

• **Great Spur wheel** Main driving wheel on the vertical shaft transmitting drive to the **stone nuts** which are small cogged pinions which can be engaged or disengaged to drive the stones.

• **Governor** A regulator used automatically to adjust the **tentering** of millstones which is the adjustment of the gap between the stones, thus regulating the fineness of the meal.

CHAPTER 3

Three Mills Open to the Public
Stevington Windmill, Bromham Watermill and Stotfold Watermill

What to look for on your visit

When you visit any of these three mills you will be struck by how sophisticated milling machinery actually is. For all their rural charm these three mills reflect the ingenuity and skill of early millwrights. You will also be impressed by just how skilful the job of a miller actually is in operating a complex and potentially dangerous piece of machinery.

The three mills that are open to the public and in working order represent the state of the art of milling at different periods. Stevington Windmill illustrates milling at its simplest as it was carried out in the late eighteenth century and earlier. Technically the mill is little different from its medieval predecessors. Bromham Watermill is a rural vernacular mill, typical of the early to mid-nineteenth century. Apart from the replacement of the waterwheel, which represented the state of the art at the beginning of the 20th century, it has undergone few technological innovations since it was built. Both demonstrate how local mills served their rural communities. Stotfold, in contrast, contains the ultimate in high quality milling machinery from the end of the nineteenth century and reflects the move to a more industrial style of milling, albeit in an earlier style of building.

Stevington Windmill

Stevington Mill represents the earliest type of windmill. It is a post mill. It was built in about 1770 and stands on high ground at the eastern end of the village. It is reputed to have been the last mill in England to work solely with common sails. (Keysoe Mill worked to a later date but it was a hybrid using both plain and patent sails.) The main body, or buck, is clad with horizontal boards and the gambrel (or mansard) roof is of corrugated iron.

The sails are essentially frames for sail cloths. The cloths would have been stretched over these frames to catch the wind as described in Chapter 2. The sails, or sweeps, are the revolving arms of a windmill which are secured to the forward end of a windshaft and are turned by wind to provide power to drive the machinery. There are common sails, as will be seen at Stevington, which are frames that support the cloths and the technically superior patent sails which are shuttered self regulating sails which are designed to achieve a fairly constant speed irrespective of the wind force. None of the latter has survived in Bedfordshire. With the common sail, cloth, sacking or canvas is spread on a lattice framework as illustrated on page 27. Each sail is set separately to suit wind conditions. They may be reefed in strong winds. This means rolling up or furling to reduce the working area.

They are labour intensive to operate and cannot easily be controlled should there be an unexpected increase in the strength of the wind. It is clearly a more primitive process than that at Duloe Mill which, as described in Chapter 2, was equipped with patent sails. The sails are attached to stocks. These are tapered spars which pass through the canister which is fixed to the end of the windshaft.

The main timber of a sail is known as a whip and is strapped or bolted to the face of the stock. The longitudinal timber on the outer edge of the sails is known as a hemlath, whilst the short horizontal bars are known as cross bars.

The main body of Stevington Mill was totally rebuilt in 1921 using the original trestle, crowntree and windshaft. Only one photo has come to light which purports to show the mill as it was before 1919. The buck dates from that time and the stones were replaced then. The tentering gear was also added. According to the best available authority (*Ref 1*) the main working parts are still pre-1921; the windshaft with its massive eight-foot brake wheel, the iron wallower driving the runner stone and the hoist used to bring the sacks of grain up to the top landing.

Before 1921 the mill had two pairs of stones driven from above: a pair of stones for barley and grist work at the front of the windshaft and a pair at the tail for wheat. Following the rebuild the mill has had only one pair of stones, Derbyshire Peak stones which are more suited for grinding animal food than for quality flour. It is significant that at the time of the accident described below, they were milling beans not flour.

The body of the mill is two storeys high and clad with black weather boarding. It was turned into the eye of the wind by the miller pushing on the tailpole after he had levered the access ladder clear of the ground by means of the talthur which is the lever pivoted on the side of the tail pole, as illustrated on page 10.

In the early years of its life the mill had no roundhouse. The trestle was open to the elements as can be seen on pictures of other post mills such as Aspley Guise, referred to in Chapter 5. The mill was originally tarred, and the trestle is still coated in tar, indicating that it must once have been unenclosed.

The roundhouse appears to have been added at some time during the late 19th century to provide additional grain storage. There are bins for this purpose all around the roof space, but it would seem that they would have been difficult to fill.

Inside can be seen the massive cross of four oak beams, known as crosstrees and quarterbars, which triangulate the structure. These support the large central post from which this type of windmill gets its name.

In 1919, while the mill was working, part of the frame had collapsed causing a near disaster. Fred Harpin, the miller, vividly tells the alarming story (*Ref 1*):

It was one day in November when the guv'nor asked me to go up and grind a few bags of beans. A good wind was blowing so I clothed her up and got started. After a while the wind increased. I didn't like the way she was rocking about at all, so I called Arthur Coleman who was hedging nearby, and asked him to come up with me and there we stood rocking to and fro something awful. It was evident that something was wrong with her, and I said to Arthur: 'I am going to stop her.' I let down the brake lever and sat on it. By this time the sails were going so fast that we both got scared stiff. Nothing happened, so Arthur came and sat on the lever with me, and there we were going up and down like a seesaw, and I was afeared she might catch fire from the friction of the wooden brake on the headwheels as we couldn't slow her down at all. Arthur said 'I am not staying here any longer' and took a header down the steps, but before he got to the ground there was a crash and the mill lurched forward, throwing him off the last half dozen steps. The sails had fouled the ground bringing the old mill up with such a jolt, so out I went double quick. 'That's the last time I'm going up there 'till this wind drops,' I said. 'Nor me,' said Arthur.

It was later discovered that a side girt had broken. These are main timbers running the full length of the side of a post mill and supporting the framing of the body of the mill. This had caused the mill to fall forward. The damage was repaired in the rebuilding of 1921 and the mill continued to work until it was honourably retired in 1936/1938. The County Council acquired it in 1951.

The reconstruction of 1921 was a complex operation and it is quite surprising that it was carried out at all, bearing in mind that Stevington Mill represented a primitive and obsolete technology and little improved on its medieval forebears. Nearly all the timbers were replaced, generally in pitchpine. It appears that Percy Keech, who carried out the repair, faithfully copied the previous design.

Although an enormous undertaking it would seem that very little change was made to the basic structure. Recent evidence discovered during the recladding of 2003/4 suggests that he copied what was left from the wreckage. The fact that there was only one set of nail holes indicates that the weatherboarding and the frame were all replaced in 1921. The new body is carried by two pine beams, the side girts, of huge proportions, being 10 feet long, 16 inches deep and 12 inches wide. In addition to the repair of the frame a number of smaller jobs were carried out at the same time. The current pair of peak stones are believed to have been obtained from Milton Ernest Watermill, whose machinery was being removed at the time, The stones are four feet in diameter and large for a windmill and are thought to be more suited to a watermill which would support the idea that they came from Milton Ernest. A spare millstone was placed at the back of the mill to improve the balance of the mill and help counterbalance the sails. Another one has since been set in the floor of the roundhouse as an exhibit. At the same time the mill was fitted with a new tentering device by a millwright from the firm of Thomas Course & Sons of Bedford.

In recent years the mill has received much attention. The weatherboarding has been substantially renewed and significant repairs have been made to the brakewheel with two sectors being replaced. The sails have been replaced several times over the years, notably in 1958 and 1985 when new sails were attached to the old stocks. As many people will remember, they were painted white. In 1996 one of the stocks holding the sails snapped, damaging itself and the lower adjacent sail. A new set of sails, which are stained rather than painted, was installed in September 2004. These are of as close a design as possible to those that are shown in photos immediately post 1921. They have been provided with cloths so that on special occasions the sails can be seen revolving again in the traditional way as illustrated on pages 65 and 66. They have a span of 61 feet and only just clear the ground when rotating (*Ref 2*).

What to see at Stevington Mill
The body of the mill, often known as the buck, can be rotated round the post so that the sails, or sweeps, could catch the wind from whatever direction it might come. In order to do this the miller would have to raise the flight of steps clear of the ground, using the thalthur, and lean against the tail pole.

A steep ladder leads to the interior where you can see milling at its simplest. Mr Harpin could remember carrying a 16 stone sack up these steps. You enter the lower of two floors where the meal was processed. Climb the internal ladder and you arrive on the stone floor. The sails drive the massive brakewheel with its 98 apple wood teeth which fits tightly under the gambrel roof, a form well suited to accommodate the brakewheel. This wheel has a clasp arm method of construction where parallel, rather than radial, spokes enclose the windshaft, and are held tight by wedges. The windshaft is inclined at 7.5 degrees to the horizontal. The brake can be seen tightly gripping the circumference. Its function is to control the speed of the machinery. The iron wallower is meshed with the brakewheel and drives the upper of the pair of stones via the stone nut. This is made of cast iron and has 18 teeth. The stones themselves are enclosed in a wooden vat which prevents the flour being flung far and wide by centrifugal force. Under normal wind conditions, when the sails revolve at 12 to 15 revolutions per minute, the upper stone (the runner) would revolve at 65 to 80 rpm.

Sacks of grain would be hoisted up through the trap doors in the floors. Grain would be fed into the hopper on the right hand side from where it rolled down the sloping chute known as the 'slipper'. Its angle could be adjusted to control the speed at which the grain was fed to the stones. The grain would be ground between the stones and was fed to bins on the lower floor. The rope on the windshaft could be attached to the stones so that they could be lifted by wrapping a rope round the windshaft and turning the windmill into a manually powered crane. Rotating the sails by hand allows the precise control needed for this operation.

On the lower floor of the buck there is a meal bin/trough which was fed from the stone vat on the floor above via the spout which can be clearly seen. The speed governor can also be seen. This is an automatic device regulating the speed at which the stones turned. It is particularly useful in gusty conditions in controlling the speed of the machinery and ironing out the inconsistencies of wind power. It also adjusts the gap between the runner and the bed stone. As the wind picks up and the sails go faster the stones come closer together. This increases the friction and hence acts as a brake. Regulating the speed by adjusting the gap between the stones is however only achieved at the expense of inconsistency of the meal. This may however not be a problem if only animal feed is being produced.

Within the roundhouse can be seen the basic triangulated structure which supports the buck and enables it to be turned to face the wind. Between them they support the vertical main post which projects upwards to the intermediate floor of the buck. The buck is supported by a bearing on top of the main post, and is kept in place by a pintle, a projecting piece of iron centred on the bearing. This bearing takes the whole weight of the buck and is the point on which the buck is turned. There is also a bearing at the top of the quarter bars. Its function is to control horizontal movements.

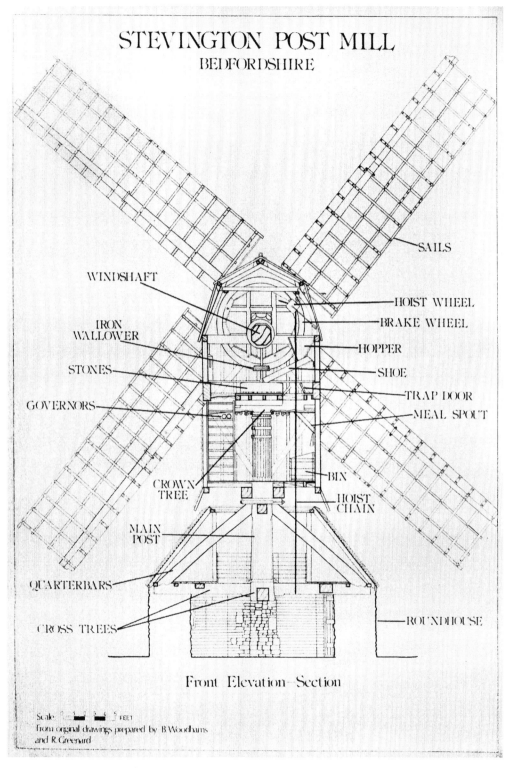

STEVINGTON POST MILL
BEDFORDSHIRE

SAILS

WINDSHAFT

HOIST WHEEL

BRAKE WHEEL

IRON WALLOWER

HOPPER

STONES

SHOE

GOVERNORS

TRAP DOOR

MEAL SPOUT

CROWN TREE

BIN

HOIST CHAIN

MAIN POST

QUARTERBARS

CROSS TREES

ROUNDHOUSE

Front Elevation Section

Scale ▬▬ ▬▬ FEET
From original drawings prepared by B.Woodhams and R.Greenard

Measured drawing of Stevington Windmill by Brian Woodhams prepared for RIBA examinations.

Turning now to the watermills at Bromham and Stotfold, the aspects of the process to see at these two mills are:

How the power of water is harnessed through waterwheels

Waterwheels take a variety of forms depending on the volume of water available and the fall of the river. Overshot wheels, as at Stotfold, are considered to be more efficient than undershot wheels or breastshot wheels. The wheel at Bromham, however, is a superior one displaying the state of the art at the beginning of the 20th century. The energy to turn the waterwheel is supplied by the mill pound (or pond) immediately upstream. A sluice (or penstock) allows the water to drive the paddles or buckets and so turn the wheel. When the sluice is opened water cascades onto the wheel, either striking the paddles or filling the buckets, thus forcing the wheel to revolve. Waterwheels are sometimes contained within the main mill building as at both Bromham and Stotfold and sometimes outside it as at Flitwick and Astwick.

How the power is transmitted to the millstones

This involves transferring power from a horizontal shaft to a vertical shaft. In the case of the watermills this is done through gear wheels known as the pit-wheel, the first gear wheel inside the mill which meshes with a wallower, a cast iron bevel gear wheel which transfers the drive from the pit wheel to the main vertical shaft. A further great spur wheel drives one or more pinions known as stone nuts which turn the stones themselves.

The hurst is the massive timber or iron framework in a watermill which holds the main gearing in place and supports the millstones on the floor above. Usually there is a crown wheel on the stone floor which may drive a lay shaft for driving ancillary machinery. In watermills this machinery is at the lowest level of the mill whist in windmills it is at the very top.

How the grain is turned into flour or meal

Flour is used for baking and meal for feeding animals. The grain is raised to the top of the mill by use of a sack hoist where it could be stored before being fed down to the stones for milling. This is generally known as the bin floor. It is a gravity-fed process. Nowadays the grain usually arrives in a precleaned state. However, in days gone by one of the first tasks would be to separate the grain from dust and chaff in a winnower or separator before grinding could begin. A smutter is a device for removing 'smut' which is a small black fungus from the grain prior to milling.

The grain is fed down to the stone floor to a hopper on a horse above the stones

The external waterwheel at Flitwick Mill. *photo Beds CC Photographic Unit*

Grain separators at Hyde End Mill. *photo Luke Bonwick*

and thence into the centre, or eye, of the upper, or the runner stone. The stones should never touch and maintaining a minimal gap demanded constant attention. The rotation of the runner stone over the static bed stone would grind the grain into flour or meal which would fall away from the sides of the stones into the vat or tun (the wooden casing of the stones), down another wooden chute into a meal sack on the floor below which is known as the meal floor. There may also be ancillary machinery for processing, or dressing, the flour on the floor above.

Flour dressers were used to separate the wholemeal flour, as delivered from the millstones, into different grades. The most common form is known as a boulter, consisting of an inclined cylinder on which boulting cloths of varying weaves could be attached. They may be made of silk for fine flour or mesh for coarser meal. Where silk was used it was important that they were changed regularly as silk is not renowned for its hard wearing quality and a worn silk could allow husks or offals to get into the refined flour. If this happened it would reflect badly on the miller's ability to provide a quality product.

Bromham Watermill

Bromham watermill lies beside the River Great Ouse. It is a most agreeable building, which is listed Grade II, on an attractive site next to the medieval Bromham Bridge with its long causeway. The bridge is thought to date from the 12th century and the causeway over the flood plain with flood arches dates from 1813–14. The bridge was widened to its present width in 1902 on its south side. The oldest part faces the mill. There are five arches, two of which serve the mill. The Bromham bypass was opened in 1986 which removed the long distance trunk road traffic from the immediate vicinity of the mill. This now means that an atmosphere of peace and tranquillity prevails, with a vastly improved situation for pedestrians on the bridge and at the mill and its surroundings.

The mill is a part two-, part three-storey building in stone and red brick vernacular with some half timbering. The dates 1695 and 1722 appear on the stonework of the lower part of the half timbered section, but these probably reflect the levels of particularly high floods rather than dates of construction which may be of an earlier date. The working part of the mill at the east end is three storeys high built mainly of brick and straddles the two mill leats. The stone part to the west bears the date stone 1858 which records a considerable rebuilding of a much older substantial stone structure. The mill has been renovated by Bedfordshire County Council since it was acquired more than thirty years ago.

The water wheel, manufactured in 1908 by B Anstee of Kempston, is in working order and drives two pairs of stones. The other wheel was mainly wooden with a cast iron shaft. It had been damaged by ice before the Second World War. It used to drive a further three pairs of stones. All these are still in place but without their tuns or stone furniture.

Water power was used exclusively until 1930, when a Petter oil engine was installed to give power when the water level was too low. Increasingly, the engine powered more of the machinery of the mill and the water wheels were used less often as the stream became silted. By the late 1930s electric motors provided

Bromham Mill and Mill House from the causeway after a snowfall before the bridge was widened in 1902. *by kind permission of the Bedford Museum*

the bulk of power to the wide variety of other milling equipment. The original weir was at the top of the island. After 1935 the Great Ouse River Board did not allow the water to be used for milling when the water level in the river fell below a certain level. In 1981 the weir was rebuilt on its present site and this allowed more water to reach the mill.

For much of its history the mill belonged to the Manor of Bromham. During medieval times it would have ground the lord's grain and his tenants would have been obliged to have their grain milled there exclusively for a charge, an essential part of feudal obligations. Only during the post medieval period would it have become a more commercial operation. The estate was broken up in 1925. The firm R Quenby and Son bought it and owned it until 1940 when, under the threat of compulsory purchase, they sold it to the Great Ouse River Board and leased it back until 1960. They moved into the mill house where the young family led a carefree existence. The children not only had the mill and river for play but also smallholdings with pigs, poultry, horses and calves. Allegedly when no one

The yard at Bromham Mill in the late 19th century. The man in the doorway to the mill is thought to be William Orpin, the miller for 50 years. *photo The Beds CC Heritage Records*

was watching they used to ride on the sack-hoist between floors. The British Oil Cake Manufacturers, a subsidiary of Unilever, acquired the business in 1960 and withdrew operations from the site in 1971. The County Council bought the mill in 1973 from the Great Ouse River Board. The mill was by then in a very dilapidated condition and was occupied by squatters who produced pottery and leatherwork. In Feb 1974 fire broke out in the upper floor storeroom. The fire was caused, according to the Fire Brigade, by overheating of electric cables due to overloading by use of electric fire or presence of local resistance due to poor jointing of cables. By the time it was brought under control it had destroyed the roof and upper floor at its eastern end. All this has been restored using the old timbers wherever possible.

In 1980 the milling machinery was restored to working order by PH Gormley, millwrights and engineers of Hatton, Derbyshire. And in March 1983 the mill was opened to the public. In 1998 the mill began for the first time to produce its own flour, once again using the original stones and water power (*Ref 3*).

A Tour of the Mill

If the water wheel is turning when you enter the mill you are immediately aware that the waters of the River Great Ouse are rushing through the building.

The ground floor of the mill contains the iron low-breast shot waterwheel 14 feet in diameter and 6 feet 4 inches wide with thirty two curved iron buckets. Many of these have been replaced since the County Council acquired the mill. They are shaped to obtain the maximum hydrodynamic efficiency. The wheel was restored to full working order in 1980. The flow of water is controlled by a sluice which is operated by a wheel adjacent to the hurst frame. The sluice gate controls the amount of water power. There is further refinement in the form of an inclined sluice running in curved channels which provides a more forceful jet of water. It is known as a Poncelet sluice (*Note page 64*). It increases power so that one can grind faster or to grind finer at slower speed. Getting the feed rate correct is one of the skills of the miller. It is a curved gate operating in a concentric arc with the wheel. It is said to increase the efficiency of the wheel by 30% over more conventional sluices.

The wheel drives two pairs of stones on the floor above, both of which are in full working order. The shaft from the waterwheel drives a cast iron pit wheel which is 7 feet in diameter with ninety-two teeth. The drive then moves from the horizontal to the vertical by means of the wallower and is the lowest wheel on the upright shaft. It is a cast iron gear wheel 3 feet in diameter with thirty-six teeth. Mounted above the wallower is the great spur wheel. It is 7 feet in diameter with eighty-eight wooden teeth. Wood is used for two reasons: the first is that it is better to mesh cast iron with wood in the interests of noise and wear and the second that if for any reason an obstruction occurred bringing the machinery to a halt a few wooden teeth would be stripped off, which would be easier to repair than a fractured cast iron gear wheel. Note that all this machinery is held in place by the hurst frame constructed from massive oak beams which contrasts with the iron frame at Stotfold. There is evidence of panels which could be attached to the hurst frame in order to enclose the gear wheels and protect them from the inevitable dust which arises in mills. There is no evidence at Bromham that any dust extracting equipment was ever installed. Also to be seen on this floor are the wooden chutes which feed the flour from the millstones above into sacks which could be attached to these chutes. The great spur wheel meshes with the stone nuts which are 16 inches in diameter and have sixteen teeth each. Note also the tentering gear which controls the space between the millstones.

Each stone nut drives one of the two pairs of millstones, 4 feet in diameter, and both made of millstone grit on the stone floor above. The original vats, hoppers and other 'stone furniture' were destroyed in the fire of 1974 and have been replaced. The 'stone furniture' consists of a circular casing or tun around the stones. A glass window has been inserted in one of them so that the turning stones can be seen. On top a hopper is supported by a wooden framework known as a 'horse'. The shoe feeds grain from the hopper to the central 'eye' of the millstones. Its gradient can be adjusted to control the rate of flow of the grain by means of crook strings which can be operated from the floor below. Note also the iron damsels, a device to vibrate the grain feed shoe, to ensure a constant flow and to prevent the risk of the stones running dry with the attendant risk of fire through sparks igniting flour dust which can be an explosive mixture. Between the two sets of millstones the shaft continues upwards to a cast iron crownwheel 3 feet 6 inches in diameter which meshes with a bevel gear to drive a lay shaft. This drives a sack hoist and, in the past, possibly a silk dressing machine; but there is no firm evidence of this. Also on this floor is a small exhibition of milling equipment and a collection of traditional grain sacks bearing the names of several Bedfordshire mills.

The sack hoist enables the heavy sacks of grain to be lifted by power to the top of the building, to be stored in bins before being fed down to the granary floor for grinding via wooden ducts. The hoist, which is over the west waterwheel, is a reconstruction employing a sliding jockey pulley which tensions the belt. There are also the remains of a screw auger which would have enabled the grain to be fed to the appropriate bin. This floor was typical of a trading mill, with grain and meal bins on either side of a raised gallery running the full length of the mill. All of this was lost in the fire. This floor is not open to the public.

Conclusion

The future of Bromham Mill as a working watermill now seems assured and future generations will be able to enjoy a mill here for many years to come. It is intended that milling will form an important part of the future at the mill, either through regular demonstrations or even to produce flour for bread baking on site if a viable means of production can be developed. The mill has survived many changes over the centuries and new innovations will form a part of the next instalment in its rich and varied history. Meanwhile a variety of possibilities are being examined for the complex of buildings as a whole to generate revenue. This may include compatible elements such as a restaurant, craft workshop, conference facilities, farmers' markets or an art gallery. The popular picnic area is in a low lying water meadow adjoining both the mill pond and the Stagsden Brook. The banks of these watercourses support rich vegetation typical of water meadows. As so many water meadows have been lost to intensive agriculture the retention of this one is particularly valuable.

Stotfold Mill

The River Ivel is 20 miles long from its source near Baldock to its confluence with the Great Ouse at Tempsford. It enters the county just south of Stotfold where Stotfold Mill, otherwise known as the Old Mill, Upper Mill or Randall's Mill, forms an impressive complex on a bend in the road which runs past the front of the mill. It has always been regarded as one of the county's best watermills. It has been described as important because it demonstrates the development of a particular skill and technology. In 1987 the planning inspector, considering the case for converting the mill into a dwelling, emphasised that the machinery showed how the watermill was modernised and steam power added. He considered the mill and its machinery to be of national importance and was particularly impressed by the quality of the millwork. He commented that the building complex was an attractive group of buildings and an important local landmark. He also recognised its value as one of few local building groups which have architectural or historic character.

From left to right when facing the buildings there is the wagon shed, then the building of the former roller mill, dating from 1902. These are in separate ownership and the roller mill building has been a private house since 2003. Then there is the main mill building of local gault brickwork and weatherboarding and a slate roof with the tall chimney of the boiler house emerging from behind. The 18th century mill cottage and mill house is on the right and finally on the far right is the former stable block, now known as the Coach House. Stotfold Mill had been rebuilt after a fire early in the 19th century in the style of a rural mill of the period. It enjoyed the benefit of being entirely re-equipped with high quality millwork in the 1890s which enabled it to carry on operating successfully long after most other mills in the area had closed down. But eventually dwindling economic prospects led to Stotfold's last mill ceasing milling operations in 1966. They were not to be resumed for another 40 years.

The Randalls were an old established Stotfold family. John Randall, who took over running of the mill in 1876, had been trained as a miller at Jordan's Holme Mills at Broom near Biggleswade. He had clearly learned the advantages of up to date technology. After he had purchased the mill in March 1888 he made improvements which included the installation of the steam engine and the chimney, 65 feet tall, at the back of the mill to provide additional power to the waterwheel,. He also installed an additional two pairs of stones, powered exclusively by a 10 horse power steam engine, which were driven from a shaft that ran along the back wall from a large pulley to where the lift now stands. A new Robinson's separator was installed on the first floor. In 1897 he commissioned a major refit. The current

The mill complex at Stotfold in its original form. From left to right, the roller mill, the mill itself and the mill house.

waterwheel was designed, built and installed by John Lampit of Hemel Hempstead. There was also a new pit wheel, the name of whose builder is cast into one of the spokes – J Burroughs of Clophill. His final improvement was the installation of the cast iron hurst frame because the previous one would have been inadequate to cope with the additional power from the new waterwheel. The hurst is the work of Whitmore and Binyon, a leading firm of millwrights from Wickham Market in Suffolk. This company was established in 1780 and gained a reputation for high quality mill work until its closure in 1901. These improvements proved to be a sound investment and enabled the mill to prosper as a flour mill and latterly for producing animal feed. The planning inspector, referred to above, concluded:

It is clear to me that this refit brought the mill to the absolute peak of perfection for the traditional grinding of flour by mill stones.

However, the decision to build a new roller mill was less successful. Several of the other Ivel mills had been rebuilt as industrial mills, generally with large overshot waterwheels. Holme Mills even replaced its waterwheels with a turbine. Randall's new mill was simply not big enough to produce the volumes that these other mills could manage. It could not achieve the economies of scale of its rivals. It also lost out to other mills that were closer to stations on the Great Northern Railway. Members of the family owned the mill from 1876 until 1985 when the last miller Sam Randall sold it. Sam died in August 2006 but he lived long enough to see the major part of the restoration completed and the first flour produced in the April of that year. Throughout the restoration he had given invaluable help in identifying equipment salvaged from the wreckage.

The fire and its aftermath

The story of Stotfold Mill changed for ever on 15th December 1992, the most traumatic day in the life of the mill. For that was when the building was devastated in a huge fire. The Biggleswade Chronicle reported:

A two-hundred-year-old mill was razed to the ground early on Tuesday morning after fire swept through its 18th-century timber frame.

Now all that remains of the once proud landmark situated on the River Ivel in Stotfold is a charred wreck.

Following the fire an assessment was made by the Society for the Protection of Ancient Buildings to ascertain how much had survived, to assess its significance and to determine how the important remaining elements of the mill might be conserved in as sympathetic a way as possible. The report initially made gloomy reading:

In strictly architectural terms, this listed building is an almost complete loss. Part of the mill's importance, however, was as a member of a group of buildings, with watermill, house for steam engine and boiler, chimney, roller mill, wagon sheds etc. Much of the engine and boiler house still stands and the other structures are untouched. Since the ground floor of the watermill has survived, together with the waterwheel, main pit-gear, hurst frame and steam engine drive, much of the cohesion of the mill complex remains, so that each unit of this group of buildings is still vital to the integrity of the whole.

However, the news was not entirely hopeless. The report went on:

The brickwork of the lower part of the mill has survived well, although there is naturally a certain amount of spalling and mortar destruction. The waterwheel, wheel-shaft and pitwheel seem to have been unaffected by the fire, so that the prime power source remains for future use. The cast iron hurst structure has protected the remainder of the pit-gear, and the four spindles with their stone nuts, jacking apparatus, etc all appear to be in workable condition. The intensity of the fire has charred the upright shaft from top to bottom, as well as the great-spur wheel, but enough remains to be used as patterns in any reconstruction. In addition, the steam engine drive on the ground floor is still intact, only one set of bevelled cogs requiring replacement.

The use of the word reconstruction gave hope that all was not lost and the mill was ultimately spared the fate of site clearance and redevelopment for housing. English Heritage re-listed the whole complex and included the machinery in the listing.

From the vision of 1992 to the completion of restoration in 2008

Immediately after the fire Robin Tasker and Ron Roper set about the task of seeing what could be done to prevent a total loss and to see that any rebuild would be sympathetic to the site. The means for achieving this was to form the Stotfold Mill Preservation Trust whose purpose was to buy the ruin, with the long term aim of restoring it to a fully operational mill. Eventually, in 1998, the Trust acquired the mill and work could begin clearing the site and subsequently rebuilding the mill and restoring the machinery.

On a wet Saturday afternoon six years after the fire a group of volunteers walked through the gate, forced their way through the large tangle of bushes that had taken root, climbed over piles of ash and rubble and reached the remains of the broken and rusting machinery. Week after week a total of 60 tons of ash and rubble were dug out by hand from the ground floor. All the material was sieved to ensure that any items that either could be used in the reconstruction or which had historical significance, were not lost. Many pieces of machinery were salvaged and identified. A large number of original locally made bricks, for instance, were salvaged to be reused later in the rebuilding. It was also a question of recording what could or could not be retained. All this was against an intense sense of sadness and loss at what could never be regained.

The first task of the Trust was to formulate a feasibility study and business plan which subsequently resulted in several grants and donations enabling the reconstruction to begin. The work of rebuilding and restoration fell into two main categories: rebuilding the mill under the direction of John Hyde whose company was the main contractor, and restoring the machinery under Ron Roper and Phillip Radford.

The Trust began by putting together a financial package to enable work to begin. This started in 1999 with a donation from Mid Bedfordshire District Council and this enabled the Trust to obtain a grant from EB Bedfordshire (the administrators of the land fill tax) in 2000. With the first of the major grants secured, the rebuilding of the mill could begin. The shell was completed in March 2002 and a traditional topping out ceremony was held. That May, during National Mills Weekend, the building was opened by Sam Randall and County Councillor and Chairman of the Trust, John Saunders, and blessed by the Vicar of St Mary's Church, Stotfold.

The next grants from Shanks First GrantScape and WREN (all from land fill tax) enabled the fitting out of the building and restoration of the machinery. A further success for the Trust was securing a grant from the Heritage Lottery Fund to restore the milling machinery to full working order. This was a major task undertaken by Neil Medcalf, a traditional millwright, in conjunction with the local team. This marked a significant step towards the ultimate aim of producing stone ground flour once more.

The Trust managed to mobilise a large number of local people both to raise funds and to help with the restoration. While work on the fabric of the building progressed, volunteers tackled the machinery. The build-up of lime-scale on the water wheel, some two inches thick in places, meant that it could not be turned, and some of the buckets had suffered fire damage. The buckets, some 104 in all, were cut back and volunteers spent nearly ten months chipping off the lime-scale using hammers and chisels; it is estimated that some one-and-a-half tons of lime scale were removed. The wheel eventually ran in its un-restored state under water power in May 2003 and in its fully restored state in 2006.

Meanwhile volunteers wire-brushed the cast iron support columns of the hurst frame and structural steelwork to remove years of accumulated grime and rust. The millwright's work included replacing the waterwheel's sole plates (the wooden blocks that fit under the bearings to act as a cushion), fitting new buckets where necessary and making and installing a new upright shaft. Local volunteer Ray Kilby built an entirely new Great Spur Wheel, a truly stunning piece of craftsmanship, to replace the one destroyed by the fire. The rim and spacers were constructed from oak with hornbeam being used for the teeth.

The fire had damaged all four sets of millstones. Fortunately, set number two, a pair of French burr stones, had been closed (i.e. the runner stone had been lowered onto the bedstone thereby preventing the fire getting to the running surfaces) and could be salvaged and restored. All of the steel banding was corroded beyond further safe use (they have to withstand a considerable amount of centrifugal force) and the heat of the fire had destroyed the plaster backing which was no longer helping to hold them together.

A team led by Philip Radford set about the task of restoring the stones. New steel bands were fitted to the bed and runner stones and re-backed using 200 kilos of plaster of Paris. The restoration of this pair of stones was possibly the first time a French stone has been rebuilt in the UK.

The old upright shaft and great spur wheel was understood to have survived the fire 150 years earlier and was initially thought to be reusable, but further examination revealed that it had decayed to the point where any pressure on it would probably have twisted it in two. A new one was required but no suitable timber could be found in the UK. With the approval of the Society for the Protection of Ancient Buildings, a laminated shaft of Siberian larch was made in Denmark using a construction technique which has been successfully used on Dutch windmills for over 50 years. The shaft is both strong and stable. As the shell of the building was complete, the old shaft was easily cut into sections and removed. Getting the new one in was more of a problem, and holes had to be cut in all of the floors and a section removed from the roof. Using a large crane, the new shaft was lifted and lowered through the roof and into place and located in the bottom bearing. The whole job only took half an hour because of extensive preparation work.

With the waterwheel restored, new pit tank in place, upright shaft replaced, new spur wheel installed, mill stones rebuilt, crown wheel repaired and all metal work cleaned and painted, Stotfold Mill was ready for action. On Wednesday, 12 April 2006 the mill produced flour for the first time since 1966, a huge moment for all those involved and a day never to be forgotten. And on 17th November the restored mill was formally reopened by His Royal Highness the Duke of Edinburgh.

One of the Trust's achievements is to have included as many as possible of the original parts in a building which, externally at least, closely resembles the original. Clearly, beyond the ground floor this is a new mill building but one which meets the needs of visitors and has the advantage over most other mill buildings in being fully accessible for the disabled. It meets all modern standards for public access, health and safety and environmental health including a wheelchair lift to give access to the upper floors and toilets.

The restoration of the mill has been achieved in the first place by grants totalling £550,000. However, the biggest contributions have been the work and fundraising of local volunteers.

Recognition

In 2001 and 2003 the Trust won the Environmental section of Vauxhall's Griffin Award, presented annually to "organisations which make an outstanding contribution to the community through the development of a new or enhanced service or project within the following categories – Community Development, Environment or Safety and Security". In 2004, the Trust was a National Gold Award Winner in the Environmental class of The Green Apple Civic Pride Awards, which celebrate "outstanding environmental performance by recognising and publicising companies, corporations and individuals who are making an effort to preserve and protect the environment for generations to come". And in 2006 the Trust won a highly prestigious SPAB plaque.

However, there is still much to do as funds allow. The mill had four sets of stones, but only one set of stones and running gears is in working order; the next aim at this stage is to obtain a second set and make them operational too.

Mill Meadows

The mill is further enhanced by the adjacent eight-acre Mill Meadows, leased from the County Council. Teasel, the local conservation group, is working closely with the Trust and the Ivel and Ouse Countryside Project to develop a nature reserve. The result will be a varied riverside wildlife habit which is already attracting a wide range of birds, insects and animals. The group has planted many indigenous trees and hedges, created an osier bed, built an otter holt and excavated lakes and ponds, all with the aim of making the Meadows accessible to the public as a further attraction for visitors to the mill.

A Phoenix Arisen

Robin Tasker and Ron Roper had the vision from the beginning to buy and restore this magnificent building to its former glory, and see it once more standing astride the River Ivel. Robin is now the Honorary Life President of the Trust and is delighted to see their dream and vision turned into reality.

The achievement of the Trust has been to conceive a sound business plan and put together a robust financial package to enable the vision to be realised. The mill that in 1998 was valued at £1 is now worth a conservative £1.5M. The value of grants and additional materials purchased by the Trust is £750K. this means that volunteers have added a further £750K to the value.

As John Hyde, Vice-Chairman of the Trust, commented 'The members of the Trust, volunteers and all those involved with the restoration of Stotfold Mill can be rightly proud of their achievements. It has been a privilege to be part of this team and to see the building and machinery rise from the ashes.' (*Ref 4*)

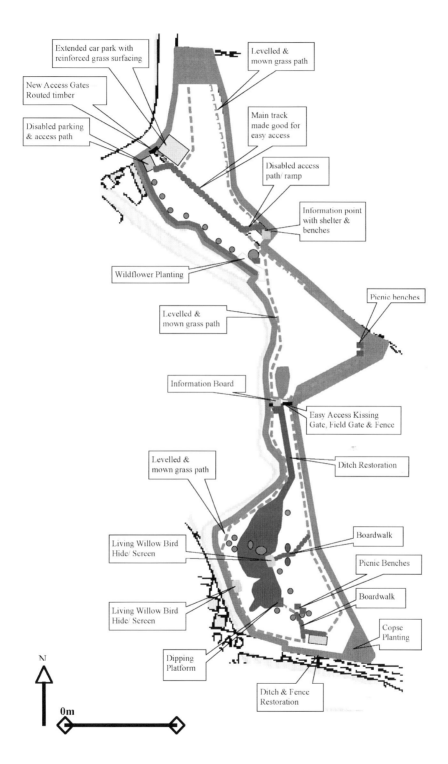

Extended car park with reinforced grass surfacing

Levelled & mown grass path

New Access Gates Routed timber

Main track made good for easy access

Disabled parking & access path

Disabled access path/ ramp

Information point with shelter & benches

Wildflower Planting

Picnic benches

Levelled & mown grass path

Information Board

Easy Access Kissing Gate, Field Gate & Fence

Levelled & mown grass path

Ditch Restoration

Living Willow Bird Hide/ Screen

Boardwalk

Picnic Benches

Living Willow Bird Hide/ Screen

Boardwalk

Copse Planting

N

0m

Dipping Platform

Ditch & Fence Restoration

There are plans for enhancing Mill Meadows just upstream of the mill.

A Tour of the Mill

The mill has three floors containing the machinery of the mill and a bin floor in the roof space which is not open to the public for reasons of health and safety relating to the limited headroom.

The ground floor The visitor will at once be impressed by the waterwheel, the massive hurst frame and the gear train. The quality of the millwork is self evident. The waterwheel is fully balanced with weights attached to the rim and runs 'like silk'. There is an exceptionally wide overshot waterwheel measuring 14 feet wide by 8 feet in diameter and is allegedly the widest waterwheel of any corn mill in the UK. It replaced the previous undershot wheel. The buckets are divided into four bays by the use of five sets of rims and spokes. There are twenty-six sheet-iron buckets for each bay which use the force of the water as well as its weight. The head of water to turn the wheel is provided by raising the sluice immediately above the wheel, forcing the water over the sill onto the overshot wheel. The scientific design of the waterwheel ensures that a maximum of power can be extracted from the river. With a good head of water this can be as much as 20 HP. The controls for the sluice are on the left of the hurst frame. The controls for the tentering gear which alters the gap between the stones and allows adjustments to be made between coarse and fine output are built into the lower part of the hurst frame underneath the stone spindle bearings. This was all installed in 1897.

The power from the waterwheel is transmitted via an iron shaft to a vertical wheel (the pit wheel), which has wooden gear teeth morticed into the rim. It is geared to a horizontal wallower, attached to the main vertical shaft. Above this wheel on the main shaft is a horizontal great spur wheel, again with morticed wooden teeth. This was painstakingly reconstructed following the fire. A section of the fire damaged wheel is on display. It drives the four pinion wheels known as stone nuts, which can be engaged by being lowered on a supporting jack, this must only be done when the waterwheel is stationary and normally only one set of the above stones is run at any one time on the stone. Finally the visitor should note the chutes which feed flour down from the stones above into waiting sacks.

The stone floor Here the grain is fed from the bins on the top floor to be ground between the millstones which are the essential element of this floor. Most of the stone furniture ancillary equipment was lost in the fire but the horse, damsels and tun from the French burrs had luckily been removed beforehand. A painstaking reconstruction of the tuns, hoppers, shoes and damsels (three of the damsels are the originals as well as the alarm bell on the restored set) will be required for the remaining sets of stones. This involved much research including old photographs and visits to other local mills, Hyde, Redbournbury and Bromham, to study construction techniques. A further set of stone furniture comprising an original horse hopper and shoe has since been discovered at a nearby property and is on display. A replica of the miller's office is located on this floor complete with the miller himself, his desk and paperwork. The floor above is supported by cast iron columns mounted on the hurst frame which also date from the upgrading of the mill in the 1890s. Note also the water gauge on this floor giving the depth of water in the river and hence an indication of potential available power.

The dressing floor This contains an oat roller, winnower or grain cleaner and bolter or flour sifter, all of which have been donated locally to replace those lost in the fire. In order to drive all the auxiliary machinery that is needed to complete the milling process there is a system of lay-shafts, driven from a pinion which meshes with the crown wheel, that transfer the power of the water wheel to each piece of equipment.

Bin floor or gantry floor (not open to the public) This is the top level from which projects the luccam (for which there are a number of variations of spelling) which is a projecting gable or dormer enclosing the mechanism of the sack hoist. It has upward facing trap doors which allow sacks to be hauled up from vehicles waiting below but which prevent anything, or indeed anyone, from falling through. There is also an internal sack hoist to enable sacks to be hauled up within the building. These are powered from a large pulley wheel and can be controlled by a rope from the floors below. On this, the top floor, were the large storage bins from which the grain would have dropped down to the stones by gravity feed. These have not been replaced since the fire.

The restoration of the mill is now in its final stages and has to transform yet again to a sustainable self-financing "business" that opens its door to the public as much as possible. The mill offers free admission and relies on the generosity of the public through donation boxes. The mill also obtains funds from:
Randalls Tea Room – opened in 2006; Kingfisher Gift Shop – 2008; Ivel (Function) Room – 2008 available for conferences and a range of events; Tours are offered to the public on Mill Open Days; Private visits are organised throughout the year for the education of visitors of all ages; Annual Steam Fair and Country Show in May; Annual Threshing Weekend in October

As the Trust states: we are here to "Keep the Wheels of History Turning".

References

1 Woodbridge, F., 1954, 'A Windmill Saved', *Bedfordshire Magazine* Vol 4 1954

2 The material on Stevington Windmill has been compiled from Howes, H., 1983, *Bedfordshire Mills*, Bedfordshire County Council; Cirket, A.F., 1966, *StevingtonWindmill*, Bedfordshire County Council; *StevingtonWindmill*, 1975, Bedfordshire County Council; Antrobus, S., 1999, *Stevington Windmill, Chronology from 1900 & Historical Sources*, Bedfordshire County Council; Fett, A., 1996, 'Stevington Windmill Sails', *Bedfordshire Magazine* Winter 1996; the County Council's Sites and Monuments Record

3 The material on Bromham Mill has been assembled from Howes, H., 1983, *Bedfordshire Mills*, Bedfordshire County Council; *Bromham Mill, Bedford*, 1983, Bedfordshire Arts and Recreation Department; Major, J.K., 1975, *Bromham Mill, a report*; Antrobus, S., 1998, *Outline Chronology & Historical Sources for Bromham Mill*; a report by Ruth Gibson dated November 1998; the County Council's Sites and Monuments Record

4 The material on Stotfold Mill has been compiled from the Trust's own document *Stotfold Mill*; Hyde, B., 2001, *Stotfold Water Mills*; the assessment by Alan Stoyel of the Society for the Protection of Ancient Buildings after the fire; articles in *Mill News*; material from the County Council's Sites and Monuments Record including a survey by J. Kenneth Major dated 1985; a letter from the Departments of the Environment and Transport dated 6th May 1987 which refuses listed building consent for the conversion of the mill into a dwelling

Technical terms used for the first time in Chapter 3

• *Roundhouse* A circular enclosing and protecting the substructure of a post mill.

• *Cross trees* The main horizontal members of the underframe of a post mill.

• *Stocks* The tapered spars to which the sails are attached.

• *Windshaft* The main shaft of a windmill which carries the sails and the brake wheel.

• *Slipper* or *shoe* The channel that feeds the grain from the hopper to the eye of the stones and vibrated by the *damsel*.

• *Mill pond* A reservoir of water held above a mill to ensure sufficient is available for consistent milling.

• *Penstock* A sluice controlling the flow of water onto a millwheel

• *Pit wheel* The primary gear wheel in a watermill mounted on the same axle as the waterwheel.

• *Hurst* The heavy timber or iron frame containing the main gearing of a watermill and supporting the stones above.

• *Dressing* The process of separating bran and coarse particles from wholemeal to produce flour.

• *Layshaft* A horizontal shaft used to power auxiliary machinery.

• *Screw auger* An Archimedes screw revolving in a trough and used for the horizontal movement of grain.

Note General J.V. Poncelet is an unlikely character in the world of milling. Of a military, scientific and mathematical background he served in Naploleon's army. He sought to improve the mills of France through the application of technology in order to feed the army. When the war was over he found that French industry was eager to carry forward his scientific work to improve power supplies. This culminated in his design for an undershot wheel which raised the efficiency from 30% to 70%. Such are the unlikely technological spin-offs of warfare!

The sails of Stevington Windmill spinning, May 2008.

opposite above: Adrian Fett and Dave Lowe, of the Bedfordshire Conservation Volunteers, attaching the cloths to the sails on 8th October 2006. This was the first time the sails had turned with cloths on since the 1930s.

opposite below: The hopper on the stone floor at Stevington. *photo Adrian Fett*

right: Fixing new sails. *photo Adrian Fett*

below left, top: The sack hoist. *photo Adrian Fett*

below left, bottom: A detail of the stone nut. *photo Adrian Fett*

below right: Replacing teeth in the Stevington brakewheel. *photo Adrian Fett*

above: The impressive appearance of Stevington Mill in the Bedfordshire landscape. *photo Adrian Fett*

below: Entering the mill on the lower floor, the post on which the mill turns is immediately obvious. *photo Adrian Fett*

above: Bromham Watermill from the west. *photo Adrian Fett*

below: The mill from the north. *photo Adrian Fett*

left: The mill from the east.
photo Adrian Fett

below: Fitting a new curved sluice
gate at Bromham Mill.
photo Jenny Forester

opposite above: Adrian Fett
demonstrates the milling process.
The wheel operates the sluice to
control the flow of water to the
waterwheel and the crook strings
in his right hand control the flow of
grain to the millstones.
photo Jenny Forester

opposite below, left: The stone
floor at Bromham showing the
crownwheel and stone vats.
photo Adrian Fett

opposite below, right: The recently
restored sample mill at Bromham.

above: The Stotfold Mill complex in 1977/8. *photo The Stotfold Mill Preservation Trust*

below: His Royal Highness the Duke of Edinburgh discusses the restoration with Alan Stoyel, John Hyde, Paul Redwood and Robin Tasker (seated). *photo The Stotfold Mill Preservation Trust*

above: The scene of devastation on the 16th December 1992 following the fire.
photo The Stotfold Mill Preservation Trust

below: The hurst frame and machinery survived largely intact.
photo The Stotfold Mill Preservation Trust

left: The restored hurst frame, pitwheel, great spur wheel and stone nuts.
photo The Stotfold Mill Preservation Trust

below left: A stone crane holding a French burr stone. *photo The Stotfold Mill Preservation Trust*

below right: A view of the waterwheel before the restoration of the mill showing some of the 104 buckets which drive the mill.
photo Ron Roper

bottom: A recreated stone vat, hopper and shute for delivering grain from the floor above.
photo The Stotfold Mill Preservation Trust

above: The rear view of Stotfold Mill showing the Mill Meadows on the right.
photo The Stotfold Mill Preservation Trust

below: The front elevation of the mill as it is today. *photo The Stotfold Mill Preservation Trust*

above: The recreated miller's office at Stotfold. *photo The Stotfold Mill Preservation Trust*

right: The crown wheel and belt drives. *photo The Stotfold Mill Preservation Trust*

right: The sack hoist on the top floor at Stotfold. *photo The Stotfold Mill Preservation Trust*

above: Turvey Mill.
The wing on the right
is new and was part of
a package of 'enabling
development' to
preserve the original
building of brick
and honey coloured
limestone.

left: Milton Ernest
Watermill.

below: A neo gothic
arch over the tail race
at Milton Ernest.

above: Stoke Mills, Sharnbrook. The mill has been home to the Mill Theatre for many years.
photo Alex Goodbody

below: Thurleigh Windmill as it is today. *photo W and J Armitage*

Upper Dean Mill as it is today showing the new cap, replacement doors and windows and repairs to the brickwork.

above:
Flitwick
Watermill
with its
overshot
waterwheel.

left:
Astwick, or
Bowman's,
Watermill on
the River Ivel.

CHAPTER 4

The Remains of a Heritage

W e have just had a detailed look at three mills in a good state of preservation that are open for the public and where you can see something of a past lifestyle and learn about the technology that supported it. There are others that are not open to the public and the remains of several others. There are no windmills in such a complete state as Stevington but there are tangible remains of eight tower windmills. Those at Sharnbrook, Stanbridge, Thurleigh and Duloe have been converted to houses and Dunstable Mill has been converted to a centre for Sea Cadets. The tower mill at Upper Dean has been conserved and stabilised. There is also the ruin of Houghton Conquest and the remains of Shefford which is used for storage.

Windmills

Sharnbrook Windmill

This is a small tower mill built of local oolitic limestone, converted many years ago into an observation tower. It was of three floors with two pairs of 4 ft stones on the first floor. Frank Hipwell (*Ref 1*) explained an unusual feature:

> *One curious feature of the building, due possibly to the desire to save expense in erection, was the method adopted for turning the sails into the*

Sharnbrook Tower Mill in 1937 showing the unusual tail pole. *photo H Meyer*

wind. It was out of date even at that time, and is the only tower windmill in the county which has a tailpole attached to the revolving cap carrying the sails. These had therefore to be man-handled from the ground to correct their position. The usual method consists of a fantail mechanism fixed on the opposite side of the cap which automatically moved the sails into position when the wind veered, on the principle of a weather-vane.

The mill ceased work in about 1890 and the sails were removed in 1920. The contents were stripped out in 1967. A staircase was installed in the shell of the mill and observatory windows installed where the cap and windshaft had once been.

Stanbridge Windmill

This is a small tower mill, some 42 feet high to the top of its ogee cap but standing on a prominent ridge where it must have enjoyed a ready source of power. It had a fantail, a pair of double-sided patent sails, two common sails and two pairs of stones. It was gutted and turned into a house in the early sixties but has retained an authentic looking cap.

Now converted to a house, Stanbridge Mill as it was in 1934. *photo Royal commission on Historical Monuments, (England). H.E.S. Simmons Collection*

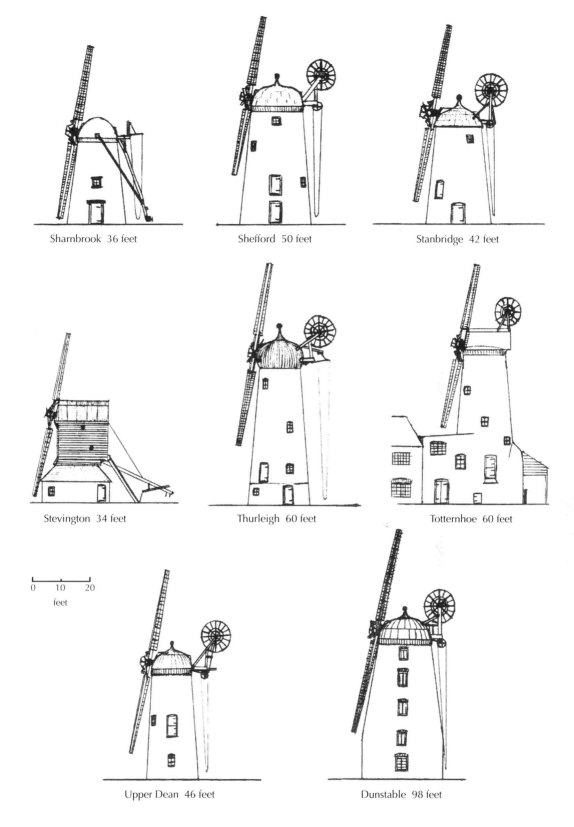

Sharnbrook 36 feet

Shefford 50 feet

Stanbridge 42 feet

Stevington 34 feet

Thurleigh 60 feet

Totternhoe 60 feet

0   10   20
feet

Upper Dean 46 feet

Dunstable 98 feet

Scale drawings of existing Bedfordshire Windmills in working order
drawn by the late Peter Dolman in 1973. *supplied by The Mills Archive Trust*

Thurleigh Windmill

This was a fine, brick built, tower mill of the Lincolnshire type standing some 60 feet high with an onion shaped cap. Originally there were two pairs of stones, one of peaks and one of burrs. One sail was blown off in 1917 and for the next 70 years the picture was one of steady decay. The other three sails together with all the iron millwork were removed for scrap in 1940 'to help with the war effort'. The roof collapsed in 1969 and, open to the weather, all the floors rotted away.

In 1983 permission was granted for it to be converted into a house and this was carried, the permission was renewed and the work carried out in 2000. As at Sharnbrook a lantern has been installed at the top of the tower providing panoramic views of the North Bedfordshire countryside. Three pairs of stones survive as does the curb track.

Dunstable Windmill

This tower mill was built in 1839 and is still a well known landmark in Dunstable. It originally had four double shuttered patent sails and was 'winded' by an eight blade fantail driving three pairs of stones. The mill was bought in 1890 by Frederick Simmons, of the well known Bedfordshire milling family. It remained in use but powered by a steam engine until just before the Second World War. It was bought in 1945 by the Sea Cadets and converted to their permanent home and named 'Training Ship Lionel Preston'.

Dunstable Tower Mill in 1935. *photo Harry Meyer*

Thurleigh Mill in 1936. *photo H Meyer*

Upper Dean Windmill shortly before consolidation works.
photo Vincent Pargeter

Upper Dean Windmill

This is a small red brick mill standing on the windswept borders of Northamptonshire. It is 46 feet high to the top of its acorn finial. When I wrote about it in the early 1980s I reported that the cap had gone and that deterioration was rapid. Two sails remained. Whilst the stocks were sound the frames were in poor condition and all shutters gone. Nevertheless its importance lies in the fact that it is the only tower mill in the county which still retains most of its machinery. A report was prepared by a leading millwright (*Ref 2*) in 2001 on the condition of the mill with recommendations for its repair. The floors had collapsed and the machinery was lying at the bottom of the tower where it had fallen. Much of it is intact or repairable. The conclusion was that:

Despite so many years of abandonment, the mill is not beyond repair, although much repair will be needed to restore it to some semblance of its working appearance.

Acting on this advice the new owners have replaced all defective doors and windows and installed a replacement cap of fabricated aluminium based on the original design so that the tower is now not only wind and weather tight but, apart from the lack of two sails and the incomplete state of the other two, looks much as it did in its heyday.

Houghton Conquest Windmill

This is a small tower mill 35 feet high and of a similar shape to that at Dunstable. The tower has degenerated over the years and is in a ruinous condition.

Watermills

As far as watermills are concerned there are the mills at Turvey and Sharnbrook on the River Ouse. The former has been converted to houses and apartments and the latter to a theatre. On the Ivel there are Astwick and Holme Mills. The latter is in a more complete state than the former. Then there are Langford Mill and Ivel Mill, Biggleswade which have

Houghton Conquest tower mill in 1933. *photo Royal Commission on Historical Monuments*

been converted to town houses and apartments respectively. Flitwick Mill on the Flit is still a complete mill. Hyde End Mill is the only surviving mill on the River Lea. On the Ousel there is Bellows Mill and, on one of its minor tributaries, is the rare combination of a wind and watermill at Doolittle Mill.

The catchments of these rivers make an interesting contrast and posed varied problems for those who built these mills. The River Great Ouse is already quite a mature river by the time it reaches Bedfordshire and provides a constant reliable supply of water power. The River Ivel, by contrast, is a small and youthful river which nevertheless has a constant flow and has provided a backbone of water power for the series of industrial mills in the east of the county.

The Ousel and its tributaries are minor brooks, subject to flash floods off the Chiltern Hills, with a limited resource which had to be husbanded carefully to provide a reliable source of power. Just across the county boundary lies Ford End Watermill, Ivinghoe, which is one of only two working watermills in Buckinghamshire. It is powered by the Whistle Brook, less than a mile from its spring line source in the Chilterns. As the mill lies below the scarp slope, the brook has a steep rate of fall and it was possible to use an overshot wheel at this mill. A millpond has been formed above the mill to impound the water and provide a more regular supply to drive the cast-iron overshot millwheel which measures 11 feet diameter by 5 feet width. The wheel turns at eight revolutions a minute which is translated into 125 rpm at the runner stone. It demonstrates that even a very minor stream can be successfully harnessed to power a mill.

The Lea is a shallow and sluggish stream whose source is at Leagrave. William Austin (*Ref 3*) dismissively describes the River Lea thus:

> *The Lea from its source to its confluence with the Thames was ever a small, unimportant, shallow and sluggish stream. It wound its tortuous course through the manor of Luton amidst rush grown marshes and bogs.*

The actual source of the Lea could vary considerably according to the level of groundwater. Nowadays its main source of supply is the outfall from the Luton Sewage Treatment Works just upstream of the mill. The flow therefore tends to be quite consistent.

Turvey Watermill

Owned by the Quenbys for many years it was converted to houses and apartments in circa 1990.

Stoke Mills, Sharnbrook

This was one of the biggest and most successful corn mills in the county benefiting from a fall of 8 feet, the biggest on the river. The present building dates from 1892 to the design of Usher and Anthony, architects and surveyors of Bedford. It is a fine tall building under a slate roof with deep eaves adorned by substantial drop finials. The two waterwheels were replaced by a turbine which could produce 50 horse. It originally had six pairs of stones but these were replaced by banks of modern 'gradual reduction rollers'.

The firm of Hipwell and Sons ran the mill from 1817 for 152 years until production of flour ended in June 1969 when it was 'silenced' as described in Chapter 1. In the post Second World War period, the Millers Mutual sought to reduce the capacity of milling by removing or destroying milling machinery. This usually meant roller mills. The arrangement was that the machinery should be scrapped and the mill 'silenced' for ever.

The complex of mill buildings has found new uses. Since 1979 the mill building has been home to 'The Mill Theatre'. The Mill House retains its name as a hotel and restaurant with views across the valley of the upper Ouse River and the former mill yard and buildings have become a business park.

Astwick Mill

This is another fine industrial style of building constructed in 1847 as a combined water and steam-driven mill. A comprehensive description from 1967 by J.K. Major states:

> The body of the mill is three storeyed on the upstream side and four storeyed on the downstream side. The walls are built of white gault bricks and have large circular headed panels forming a decorative treatment on each face. The boilerhouse with its decorative chimney stands on the other side. The roof is slated. On the north side of the mill there is an earlier building which may have been part of the previous mill.
>
> The millwork at Astwick Mill is important, for it is a fairly complete example of the millwrighting of the mid nineteenth century The overshot waterwheel is made of iron and is 16 feet wide by 16 feet in diameter [Note page 104]. Inside the wall of the mill on the main shaft, there is a nine foot diameter spur secondary gear on a layshaft. This layshaft drove the pit wheel which stands inside the octagonal hurst frame. The wallower engages with this pit wheel and turns the upright shaft of the mill. The great spur wheel on the upright shaft drives the eight pairs of stones. The hurst frame is entirely built of iron with classical detailing on the columns. A clutch exists which engaged the steam engine but all the steam plant is now missing. There is a crown wheel for the other machinery which has now gone from the upper floors.

Also known as Bowman's Mill, it is now in a fairly derelict state. The overshot waterwheel is external. The iron axle and spokes are still in place but little

The remains of the waterwheel at Astwick Mill showing its hub and spokes and its great diameter.

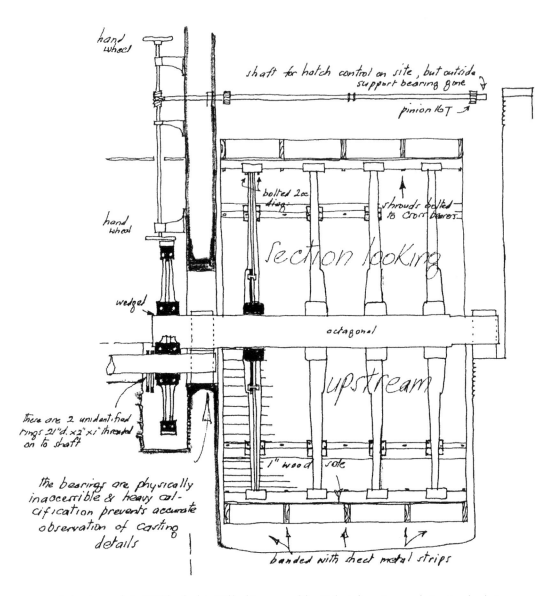

A drawing made in 1980 by the late Wilfred Foreman of the 16-foot-diameter overshot waterwheel at Astwick Mill. He commented on the bold design concept of the wheel but pointed out that the decay of the wood used in the shrouds of supporting cross bearers had led to its deterioration. He found many details obscured by heavy calcitration, a situation which has no doubt been aggravated by the passing of a further twenty-eight years. *reproduced by kind permission of the Mills Archive Trust*

remains of the buckets. The combination of a fall of about 20 feet and a massive overshot wheel must have provided the enormous amount of power needed for so many sets of stones. Of all the mills in the county this is probably the one that has the greatest potential for restoration and the most urgent need of attention. When its listed status was reviewed in 2005 it was described as:

> ...an important survival of the mid 19th century corn milling industry, and the building is one of the best preserved mills of this period in the county. It is a dated building, architecturally intact, and with sufficient machinery and surrounding archaeological evidence to read as a working mill.

Holme Mills

Holme Mills, just upstream of Biggleswade, is the county's longest surviving corn mill. It is an industrial style mill of the 1890s fully equipped with roller milling technology and powered by a 20HP Gilbert and Gilkes turbine. In the 19th century it had been powered by two overshot waterwheels, and then in 1896 these were replaced with the more efficient turbine.

John Jordan has described it:

> We have a 20 hp turbine running. It was put in by Gilbert and Gilkes of Kendal. It is an interesting old turbine. The rotor is about 10 feet diameter and it has a six inch shaft up the middle. It turns around on a piece of wood at the bottom. It is lignum vitae, the hardest wood in the world. It is lubricated by water. I thought we would lift up the turbine and see how much the wood had worn. It had worn one inch in 82 years.

At a later date the mill was additionally powered by an Allen 3 cylinder engine. This allowed wheat flour production to be raised from three sacks per hour eventually to eight sacks per hour. Both white and wholemeal flours could be produced to high standards. The mill could operate with three staff members on each shift, one on intake, the miller, and one packer.

The mill has had to be closed down because of health and safety risks. It had not been possible to reach modern standards within the confined quarters of a mill. They had had no serious injuries but the risk was always there. All the machinery is still in place. It is the only remaining roller mill in the county. All the rest were 'silenced'.

Three families have been prominent in the running of the Ivel mills. The Powers were the main force in the 19th century. Edmund Powers owned Ivel Mill, Biggleswade, Holme and Stanford Mills and his brother Charles owned

Holme Mills in 1890. It was destroyed by fire on April 14th 1899. The mill was described in the auction particulars of 1893 as with the Water Wheel, Stones, Tackle, Machinery, Going Gear, Implements and Fixtures. *photo supplied in 1984 by Mrs D Letchford of Bexhill-on-Sea, a great granddaughter of William Jordan and then aged 93*

South Mills, Tempsford and Blunham Mills. But the next generation George and Hugh suffered a series of disastrous fires in the 1880s and George was forced into bankruptcy in 1893. The mills were auctioned and the Jordans and the Franklins became the dominant names in milling in the east of the county.

William Jordan ran Holme Mills as a flour mill beyond the First World War but the mill was in poor order and was run on a shoe string: one contract was lost as there were specks of bran in the white flour. This was because the boulters or screens had not had their silks replaced. William died in 1942. The mill was derelict from 1942 to 1946, as was the mill house. His son John got the mill going again in 1946, having bought it for £5,000. John improved the running of the flour mill and also added a feed milling business.

The breakfast cereal business started in 1971 beginning with puffed wheat and puffed rice. This developed into the toasted cereals that are so well known today. Initially only health food stores were interested but by the mid 1980s the supermarkets were selling all that Jordans could produce at the mill. Several additional buildings were added to the Holme Mill complex to provide the necessary production facilities.

The appearance of the mill building itself had been much altered by the addition of a further floor and flat roof. John Jordan explained the hair-raising experience that had led him to make the change:

> When I first came here there was an ordinary pitched roof. I used to have to go out of a ventilator and luckily I used to go on a rope and clean the guttering. You get a lot of dust blowing out on the roof and it was slippery. I was right at the end and I slid off the roof and over the edge of the guttering and I said, 'If ever I get back up there I am going to put a flat roof on here.' Well, I did get back and I did put a flat roof on!

Jordans have put back a pitched roof in 1994. Many of the processes have been removed from the site which has been to some degree de-industrialised. Plans for the future include the removal of the accumulation of buildings and to return the site to something like its pre First World War state as a visitor attraction with an emphasis on the milling heritage. There is a very complete archive of the trading of the mill over many years.

Langford Watermill

The shell of this large industrial building has been converted to town houses.

Langford Mill after conversion.

Biggleswade Water Mill in about 1905, now converted to apartments. Beyond is Ivel House, home of Henry Franklin and indicative of the prosperity that a miller could enjoy. The cottage between them has been demolished to make way for Ivel Close. *photo County Record Office*

Ivel Mill, Biggleswade

Again the shell of another fine industrial building survives. A plaque reads:

> *Henry Franklin, already a coal merchant, became a miller in 1883. After a fire in 1946 the building was restored but used as a warehouse. In 1959 the business became Dalgety Franklin. In 1982 the building was converted into flats.*

As the chances of the building ever being used for milling again were minimal this seemed a most expeditious way of preserving this fine building In 1893 auction particulars described it...

> *The MILL &c (with Residence and Outbuildings), is let to Mr Henry Franklin, at the Reduced Yearly Rent of £260 And is a substantial 4-storey Building, erected of White Brick, and Slated, and worked by a Wooden-breast Water Wheel, driving four pairs of flour stones and 1 pair of Barley Stones.*

Flitwick Watermill

This is one of the more important watermills in the county. The miller's house and stables together with the mill make an attractive group of buildings. It is a three storey building. The first storey is in brick and the upper floor has ochre painted weatherboarding. There is a luccam over the mill door and the roof is slated. The mill-work is important in that it is typical of the early 19th century, though it has been repaired at various times since its erection. The cast iron overshot wheel is 12 feet wide and 10 feet diameter. The main shaft carries a cast iron pit wheel inside the main wall. This engages with a cast iron wallower on the upright shaft. Two pairs of stones are driven by the great spur wheel. A third pair of stones was driven by a steam engine but this has been removed and replaced by an electric motor. The wooden upright shaft drives a sack hoist, dressing machines and a roller from the crown wheel on the first floor.

The mill only ceased trading in 1987 and is therefore in a remarkably complete state. When its listed status was reviewed in 2005 it was described as:

…a rare surviving example of a complete milling process. While the building is not architecturally of a piece, since it has been extended and reclad, it demonstrates the continuing process of expansion and development of the 19C mill.

This mill contains a complete milling installation that reflects typical 19th century rural practice. It provides an insight into how such a mill was progressively improved to meet the changing commercial needs of the 20th century. Writing in 1967 Kenneth Major identifies patterns between the wheels of the county's waterwheels:

Many of the (larger) mills, particularly those on the Ouse and the Ivel, have two waterwheels, and the majority of these wheels are either breast shot or undershot.

Flitwick Mill therefore represents one of the few small mills to survive, its overshot wheel adding a further element of especial interest (*Ref 4*). Its survival in its present state is important as one of few mills surviving unaltered.

Barton Mill

Barton Mill is a fine timber framed and timber clad four storey building on a brick base believed to date from 1852 which is the date cast on the surviving 16 ft diameter external overshot waterwheel. The state of the art machinery has survived largely intact. It included three pairs of stones of which one pair is believed to have been French burrs and a flour-dressing machine that could produce three grades of flour including the fashionable but unhealthy refined white flour. A new mill house was built at the time together with an auxiliary post mill which was subsequently moved to Barton Hills where it survived until circa 1865 when it was destroyed by fire. From the beginning of the 20th century a steady decline set in. Conditions were further impaired by the changes to the stream that powered the waterwheel. Originally the site was well served by the converging brooks flowing from the springs of the Chiltern scarp slope. The brook eventually drains into the River Flit at Shefford. Mr LW Vass, the then owner, recalled in 1982 how the combination of the abstraction of groundwater and highway works had put paid to the prospects of milling:

> There was a considerable quantity of water coming down. The volume is considerably decreased than what it was years ago because of extraction. It (the mill) can't be put back in working order: the main reason being the stream which supplies it passed under the Barton-Sharpenhoe road. There used to be a hump bridge. The County Council wanted to get rid of that arch. And so, as the mill was not in use, they came to some arrangement to deepen the bed of the stream so that it took away the hump-backed bridge. That meant there is no longer access to water coming to the mill head.

As part of the more recent construction of the Barton bypass the millstream was lowered. The bypass means that the mill is now separated from the village and its setting has been changed by the development of a shopping village and garden centre. The shopping village would, however, seem to assure the future of the mill as a potential visitor attraction. It is open to the public during shop opening hours.

In 1982 Mr Vass described the restoration that he had carried out in 1974. The mill was given listed status at that time:

> If we hadn't done something, it would have collapsed. We replaced any of the damaged framework, reclad it entirely and also did some repairs to the roof. Most of the machinery is there but it is not absolutely complete. The gear for driving it is complete. There is one pair of millstones which is complete and one that has only got the bedstone. One set was removed and sold [presumably the more valuable French burrs].

The mill was deteriorating again when it changed hands in 1994 and again in 2001 (Ref 5). Since then repairs to the waterwheel have been carried out and the building has been renovated. The water wheel is in a good state of repair but,

Barton Mill in 1905 showing the mill pond, where the garden centre now is. The chimney served a steam engine which operated the mill when the water supply was not sufficient.

at the time of writing, it could not be worked because of a faulty bearing where the axle goes through the wall. The pitwheel, wallower, great spur wheel and stone nuts are encased in wooden framed glass screens and appear to be in good order. The flour shutes are missing. On the stone floor there are now two sets of peak stones but one runner is missing. The tuns are in place but there is no stone furniture. The third floor is sealed off because it is not safe.

The intention is to get the wheel turning by recycling the water from the tail race.

Hyde End Mill

Nowadays this is the first mill on the river Lea but in the distant past, before the growth of Luton, there were six others between it and the river's source at Leagrave.

The mill is a fine example of a mid 19th century complex of mill buildings lying to the west of the road from Luton to Wheathampstead (*Ref* 6). Its value lies in the preservation of an unusually complete range of milling equipment. In addition a comprehensive and extensive documentation has survived on site into the day to day running of the mill which includes ledgers giving an extremely detailed account of everyday transactions. These represent a unique and detailed record of the running of a rural mill at the turn of the 20th century. The mill house lies in Bedfordshire whilst most of the watermill and all the steam mill lie in Hertfordshire. The whole complex of buildings, which include the water powered corn mill, the attached granary and store, are listed as a whole and the listing includes the waterwheels and mill machinery. The complex has been well maintained and is in a remarkably good state of preservation. A steam powered roller mill plant was installed in the adjoining warehouse. The two stationary steam engines have survived intact but the roller mills were stripped out when the mill was 'silenced'.

Well used stone furniture and an unusual octagonal vat at Hyde End Mill. *photo Luke Bonwick*

Hyde End Mill in 1996. *photo Colin Bowden*

The waterwheel dates from 1932 and is of breastshot design. It is 7' 5'' wide and 13' 7" in diameter and is powered by a 5' 6" fall of water. It drives through pit wheel, wallower, great spur wheel and stone nuts to three pairs of stones that are complete with tuns, hoppers, damsels, crook strings and tentering gear. There is a wide range of ancillary equipment include screw augers, grain elevators , three grain separators on the meal floor and on the stone floor a smutter, a 'dustless milling machine' and a scourer. This suggests that money was wisely invested in the mill, probably in the 1880s. Suppliers include Whitmore and Binyon for the grain elevators and there is a 'Eureka' machinery imported from New York which combines the functions of a smutter and scourer. There is also a dustless milling machine by the same manufacturer. The impression is given of a well run business which was able to survive longer than many others. However, trade had almost completely gone by the early 1950s.

To the north of the mill is the large head pond in which water is impounded to power the waterwheel. There is a timber sluice gate which can be raised to allow some water to escape into the channel which bypasses the mill.

Doolittle Mill, Totternhoe

Doolittle Mill is served by the Well Head stream whose source is only 400 yards away on the scarp slope of the Chilterns. It is one of the most interesting mills in Bedfordshire. Such is its architectural and historic value that it has been upgraded to Grade 11*. It is an example of the extremely rare combination of a windmill and watermill.

The family of the Misses Buckmaster owned it from 1907 until 2000. I was fortunate enough to have spoken to John Buckmaster Linney, only a matter of weeks before his death in 1981. The mill was last worked in 1925 and has remained in a complete but deteriorating state ever since.

I was born in 1922 and I can't remember any milling being done at all. The mill is entirely as they left off. The sails blew off in 1868: there is an almighty wind from the west.

The loss of the windmill was a major disaster, for in subsequent years water power on its own was to prove inadequate:

They had a portable engine for the last four or five years.

said Mr Linney and there is an external wheel to take a belt drive to prove it. He had hoped that it might be possible to restore the mill to working order but the raising of funds had proved an insuperable hurdle. In 1990 a very detailed and prescriptive report (*Ref 7*) was prepared which is the most comprehensive technical appraisal of the mill. In the report, the author, Kenneth Major, hypothesised that:

The mill was a watermill to which a windmill was added in the late 19th century. The watermill was modernised with the mid nineteenth century millwork to enable it to have a greater production because of the low level of the spring fed stream.

The mill has five floors, the watermill occupying the bottom two and the windmill the top three. The windmill had two pairs of stones of which one cullen bedstone remains. The sails drove two pairs of stones and the waterwheel another two pairs. Of the windmill machinery only the upright shaft and its wooden wallower and the great spur wheel are left. The cast-iron wind shaft has been supporting the floor above the waterwheel for many years.

The two sets of stones of the watermill are still in place and complete with their stone furniture, as is most of the gearing and machinery. There is also a silk

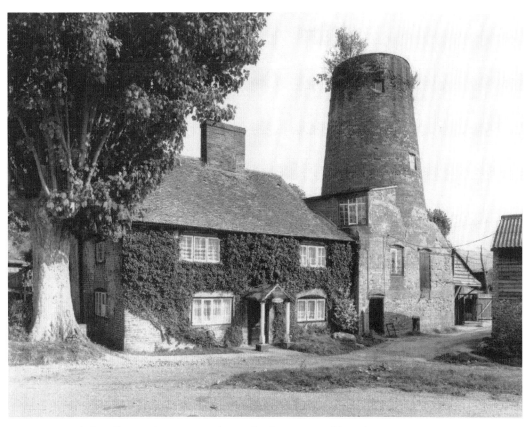

Doolittle Mill, Totternhoe in 1978. The tree has been removed from the tower in recent years.
photo Beds CC Photographic Unit

boulter on this floor. However, of the internal overshot wooden wheel, which was approx 16 feet in diameter and three feet wide, only the wooden axle and spoke hubs remain. The embanked mill pond lies behind the mill and the launder and penstock are still in place.

In the 1990 report its author Kenneth Major envisages that one day the machinery could be put in such a condition where it could be displayed to the public and possibly even restoring the mill to working order. However, it is clear from his report that a thorough overhaul of the machinery would be necessary and no up-to-date estimate of the cost of such work has been made. In addition the building as it stands presents far too many hazards for public access. During the 1990s the deterioration was the cause of increasing concern to the local authority. In 2002 the roof cap was blown off and landed some distance away in a repeat of the gale that had removed the sails over a hundred years before. As this left the interior open to the elements rapid action was necessary to replace it.

In my previous book I wrote:

Of all the decaying mills in the county the most complete – and the one offering the best hope of restoration – is Doolittle Mill at Totternhoe.

Doolittle Mill, Totternhoe. An early photograph of this unusual combined wind and watermill taken before 1868 (the year when the sails are believed to have been blown off).
photo Beds CC Photographic Unit

This view was supported by the 1990 report:

The rescue, repair and protection of Doolittle Mill is fully justified as it is such an important example. It is however at a point when it has to be rescued now or it will be lost.

Fortunately the mill found a sympathetic buyer in 2001 who has carried out a 'first phase' of restoration. The mill itself has been made weather-tight, and a new roof has been fitted. The brickwork has been renovated where necessary, particularly the top courses of the tower. Inside the mill has been cleared of accumulated rubbish and debris, and artefacts saved, the waterwheel channel and pit wheel pit have been cleared. However, it is all too clear the extent to which floorboards have been weakened and floors have collapsed, notably over the waterwheel. Some of the ladders from one floor to another lack rungs. This

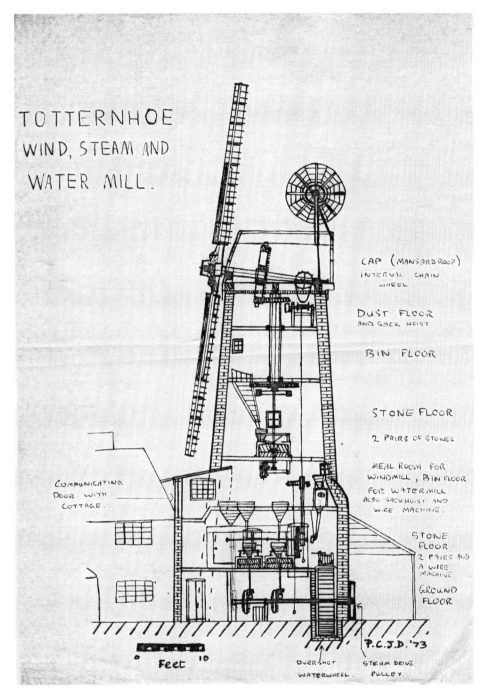

TOTTERNHOE
WIND, STEAM AND
WATER MILL.

CAP (MANSARD ROOF)
INTERNAL CHAIN
WHEEL

DUST FLOOR
AND SACK HOIST

BIN FLOOR

STONE FLOOR

2 PAIRS OF STONES

MEAL ROOM FOR
WINDMILL, BIN FLOOR
FOR WATERMILL
ALSO SACKHOIST AND
WIRE MACHINE.

STONE
FLOOR
2 PAIRS AND
A WIRE
MACHINE

GROUND
FLOOR

COMMUNICATING
DOOR WITH
COTTAGE.

P.C.J.D. '73

Feet

OVERSHOT
WATERWHEEL.

STEAM DRIVE
PULLEY.

Sectional drawing of Doolittle Mill by Peter Dolman from 1973. *The Mills Archive Trust*

raises the question of whether a financial package could be put together which would achieve some degree of restoration whilst achieving an acceptable level of public safety.

Bellows Mill

Just a short distance away on the top reaches of the River Ousel is Bellows Mill which was a working mill until 1955 when its isolated position limited capacity and its comparatively slow method of working rendered it obsolete and no longer profitable. It had been re-equipped with a turbine and high quality millwork by Whitmore and Binyon driving two pairs of stones, all of which no doubt enabled it to keep working for so long. It has been in the same family since about 1825, the Simmons who owned Flemmons Mill in Leighton Buzzard which in its time was one of the most modern in Bedfordshire. The mill has been converted into a home with a restaurant attached. The millwork and turbine survive.

Milton Ernest Mill

This is a building of architectural merit in its own right and includes several neo gothic features. Cast iron columns support the upper floors. It was designed by the eminent Victorian architect William Butterfield who was responsible for the nearby Milton Ernest Hall. The machinery was removed in the early 1920s, with the millstones allegedly going to Stevington Windmill. The 1947 floods destroyed the weir on the River Great Ouse which had diverted water into the mill stream and little water has come down the mill race ever since except in times of flood. There is evidence of a by-pass sluice nearby. The dimensions of the internal wheel pit suggest that it probably contained a low breast shot wheel about 10 feet wide. Until the 1960s the building was used for processing agricultural materials. Part of it has been a dwelling for many years and it is likely that the remainder will be converted in the future.

References

1 Hipwell, F., 1949, 'The Mills of Sharnbrook', *The Sharnbrook Review*

2 Pargetter, V., 2001, The Windmill, Upper Dean, Bedfordshire

3 Austin, W., 1861, 'The Domesday Watermills of Bedfordshire', *Bedfordshire Historical Record* Vol 111, 1861

4 Bonwick, L., 2008, Report on Flitwick Watermill on behalf of SPAB

5 Northwood, A., 'Barton Watermill', *Chiltern News* Issue 171

6 Bonwick, L., 2007, Hyde Watermill, East Hyde, Hertfordshire/Bedfordshire, Archaeological Buildings Survey Report, Bonwick Milling Heritage Consultancy

7 Major, J.K., 1990, 'Doolittle Mill, Totternhoe, Bedfordshire. A Report on the mill and its Condition'

Note

A recent measurement shows that the waterwheel at Astwick Mill is not more than 12 feet 6 inches wide.

CHAPTER 5

Gone but not Forgotten

Windmills

Biggleswade Tower Mill

This was built in 1860 and was the tallest and finest windmill in the county and a Grade II listed building. It stood in Franklin's Yard off Hitchin Street. It was 70 feet high to the top of the cap and was of the 'Cambridge' type of tower mill with an outward flared petticoat to its ogee cap. The stones were on the third floor. The cap had a gallery around it and when the mill needed tarring, sa cradle was suspended from it for that purpose. It ceased working by wind in 1931. Its sails became unsafe and were removed in the early 1950s. The remaining superstructure had deteriorated but the tower remained sound. In 1966 it was still used for milling with the aid of electric power. The owners wanted the space it occupied for the more efficient use of the site and the brickwork for hardcore in its further development. They took the view that the mill  was of no particular significance; others had been preserved so there was no useful point in keeping it. At 1966 prices £2,000 was needed for its restoration. The public authorities were unable to contribute grants and reluctantly agreed to its demolition. *photo Beds CC Photographic Unit*

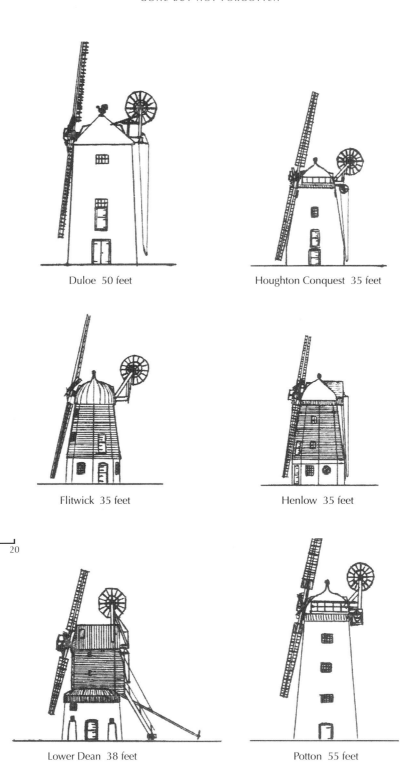

Scale drawings prepared of, apart from Duloe, lost windmills of Bedfordshire by the late Peter Dolman in 1973. *supplied by The Mills Archive Trust*

left: The final flowering of the Victorian millwright's art at Biggleswade Windmill. Underneath the cap is the massive iron brakewheel and brake. *photo Beds CC Photographic Unit*

below: The curb and guide rollers on which the cap and sails rotated to face the wind. *photo Beds CC Photographic Unit*

Aspley Guise

Primitive forebear; a small open trestle post mill with unusual vertical boarding. The photograph was taken in about 1900 shortly before the mill was pulled down. Part of one sail is missing and the mill clearly must have been out of use for some time.

Husborne Crawley Pug Mill

A scene in about 1820 by Thomas Fisher showing a rare horizontal pug mill which mixed clay for
brick making in the Crawley Kiln (centre). A water mill is on the right.
photo originally supplied by the then North Beds Borough Council

Lower Dean Post Mill

An early photograph (circa 1905) of the unusual mill at Lower Dean whilst still in working order. The oldest of a score of post mills, it survived until it collapsed in 1959. The absence of diagonal bracing is thought to have contributed to its collapse. Now only the base remains. The mill was built in 1762 and was substantially rebuilt in 1834 as a most unusual post mill called a composite mill. The buck ran on a circular cogged track around the top of the roundhouse. The fantail was geared to this track. The buck could be turned either by tail pole or fantail. Latterly the fantail failed owing to the body settling heavily on its rollers. Finally the only way to pull the tailpole round was with the aid of a donkey. *photo H Meyer*

Riseley Post Mill

Riseley Post Mill may have been the last post mill to be built in the area. It was originally an open trestle mill, having a round house added in the latter part of the 19th century. It was fairly large and not as primitive as some of the post mills in the area. *photo supplied by Andrew Gell*

Flitwick Smock Mill

Henlow Smock Mill

above: Flitwick Smock Mill is known to have been the work of Thomas Course of Bedford in about 1850 who may well have built a similar but earlier smock mill at Great Barford. It had a conical cap and a fantail. Milling ceased shortly before it was burned down on November 9th 1903. The *Bedfordshire Times* for 28th February 1852 contains the following as part of a sale notice: All that new corn windmill situate near Dennel End aforesaid, fitted with one pair French and one pair Peake 4 ft stones and flour machine. *photo from the Peter Dolman collection*

left: Henlow Smock Mill was demolished in 1935. Only the brick base remains. *photo H Meyer*

Watermills

Stanford Mill

Rare pictures of Stanford Mill, the last mill on the Flit, about which very little is known.

Kempston Mill

Kempston Mill was a particularly imposing five storey building which was destroyed by fire in 1969 and little remains. The mill hardly changed for hundreds of years until about 1900 when a roller plant was installed along with a steam engine with a tall brick chimney. John Clover recalled: 'The mill ran continuously through two World Wars, particularly during the latter.' In 1939 most of the milling capacity of the country was centred on the ports and much was destroyed in the blitz. Country mills, such as Kempston, were vital in those times. *photo supplied by J Clover*

South Mills

South Mills, Blunham was designed by the famous Bedford architect, John Usher, and was used for milling bones and slaughterhouse waste. It was demolished in 1977.
photo Beds CC Photographic Unit

Cardington Water Mill

Cardington Water Mill was built to the designs of the great engineer John Smeaton and demolished in 1936. *photo Bedford Museum*

Sandy Mill

Sandy Mill was demolished in 1977. *photo J.K. Major*

CHAPTER 6

Reflections on the Problems of Restoring and Conserving Mills

The problem of conserving and preserving buildings whose original use may have become obsolete is not restricted to mills. Most conservation officers will have wrestled, for example, with proposals for conversion of unused barns and redundant churches into dwellings. Whilst such proposals do fulfil the purpose of preserving a building and its place in a street scene, they also tend to destroy the unencumbered space which is essential to the purposes for which they were originally designed. Mills present similar but subtly different challenges. The core part of the mill is the machinery. The internal spaces are there to accommodate working machinery within a building which may in itself be of no great intrinsic merit. The listing of architectural and historic quality is usually concerned with the exterior of a building and its role in the environment as being usually more important than the interior. Furthermore listed building control has generally been restricted to the building itself and not the contents. In the case of mills this has proved often to act against the protection of their integrity as working buildings.

Mark Barnard, (Ref 1) Conservation and Historic Buildings Officer, Suffolk County Council, summarised this peculiar position relating to mills:

While some mills are listed for their attractive exteriors, the greater interest often lies within. Mills complete with their working parts are even rarer than unconverted barns, and more at risk too because a new use often poses a threat to the machinery – the very mill itself. It is therefore vital that our heritage of traditional mills receives adequate protection through listing as they are a unique blend of architecture and technology, in effect covered machines. Unfortunately, there has been a good deal of confusion over the extent to which the interior machinery and fittings of a mill are protected by listing. At best many Conservation Officers regard it as a 'grey area', the inference being that the law is unclear and the issue open to persuasive legal argument. But even the most sceptical would have to agree that it would be absurd if the machinery, whose presence can be a major factor in deciding to list the mill in the first place, could then be removed (or even altered) with impunity. Can this really be the case?

The conversion of mill buildings to residential and the preservation of machinery are often incompatible for the reasons set out by Mark Barnard. Many vernacular water mill buildings in Bedfordshire have been converted to dwellings. This has involved the removal of the machinery, with the result that the building loses its intrinsic historic interest: which is why I have chosen to ignore many of them in this book. The Government has recognised this problem (*Ref 2*) and has advised:

Patterns of economic activity inevitably change over time, and it would be unrealistic to seek to prevent such changes by the use of planning controls...The issues that are generally relevant to the consideration of all listed building consent applications are...the importance of the building, its intrinsic architectural and historic interest and rarity in both national and local terms.

The Government's advice then goes on to deal specifically with appropriate after uses:

Judging the best use is one of the most important and sensitive assessments that local planning authorities and other bodies involved in conservation have to make. It requires balancing the economic viability of possible uses against the effect of any changes they entail in the special architectural and historic interest of the building in question. In principle the aim should be to identify the optimum viable use that is compatible with the fabric, interior and setting of the historic building. This may not necessarily be the most profitable use if that would entail more destructive alterations than other viable uses. Where a particular compatible use is to be preferred, but restoration for that use is unlikely to be economically viable, grant assistance from the authority, English Heritage or other source may need to be considered. The best use will very often be the use for which the building was originally designed and the continuation or reinstatement of that use should certainly be the first option when the future of a building is considered.

This advice was issued in 1995. At the Stotfold inquiry of 1987 (*Ref 3*), to be referred to below, the inspector had already advanced a similar doctrine:

Until the possibility of a mill and/or museum use has been thoroughly investigated it is my opinion that listed building consent to convert the mill to a residential use should be resisted.

This does suggest that local authorities should apply a sequential test: the first part being to ascertain whether the use for which the building has been designed can be continued and maintained. Only if that fails, to identify an alternative optimum viable use which, in the words of the Government's advice may not necessarily be the most profitable use…The problem is that residential conversions tend to be the most economically robust alternative use from the developer's point of view but it does tend to destroy the intrinsic value of the building. In a recent case in Tilty in Essex involving a residential conversion of a Grade II* listed watermill, the Secretary of State took the view that the lack of an acceptable alternative use of the building had not been conclusively proven and that the conversion would harm more than it would save in conservation terms (*Ref 4*). The ideal must be to conserve any mill in its state as a working mill. If this is not possible there are a range of alternatives which allow the building to be conserved in its historic form. Such uses might include; an educational resource for all ages and backgrounds, as a centre for local crafts and skills, or as a community centre for a variety of functions such as conferences or weddings (*Ref 5*).

It is outside the scope of this book to examine, in detail, the economics of implementing development, a subject that I have dealt with elsewhere (Ref 6). Nevertheless it seems appropriate to conclude with some general economic observations.

Essentially there are four stages of conservation for mills

1 Minimum repairs to make a building wind and weather tight

2 Internal repairs to restore defective or rotten timber work

3 Reassembly of machinery and

4 Comprehensive repairs to a reasonable semblance of a working mill.

The cost of these stages clearly increases significantly and raises the question of what the best available economic option may be. Financing restorations and enhancements out of the gratuitous increase of value in a site through the granting of a planning permission for 'enabling development' is not new. As applied to mills this may, for example, enable at least Stage 1 to be achieved. In planning terms this may well be regarded as 'reasonable'. However, the cost of repairing and overhauling machinery is expensive and unless there is a great deal of 'enabling development' a requirement to achieve stages 2, 3 or 4 is unlikely to be considered to be 'reasonable'. It may not be possible to find appropriate enabling development that will generate sufficient surplus to restore a mill to anything like its original state. Funding from other sources is likely to be necessary to enable comprehensive restoration of the interior and the machinery.

The public inquiry into an application for listed building consent for the conversion of Stotfold Mill to three dwellings has proved to be a seminal case. The local planning authority granted both planning permission and listed building consent. Mark Barnard commented:

The extent to which listed building consent was required for the removal of mill machinery was one of the key issues at a public inquiry in 1986 into plans to convert Stotfold watermill…to residential use. The listed building application was called in by the Secretary of State following strong objections from the County Council, SPAB Wind and Watermill Section and CBA (Council for British Archaeology).

After the public inquiry the inspector reported. He recommended that listed building consent be granted for the conversion of the wagon house and granary into one dwelling each, but refused consent for the conversion of the mill itself. These recommendations were confirmed by the Secretary of State. The 'granary' was the former roller mill building which had lost its machinery many years before. Allowing its conversion to residential could be seen as 'enabling' the old mill to be preserved in its original form.

The subsequent fire in 1992 did at least clarify the place of machinery in the 'listing' process. The Society for the Protection of Ancient Buildings had taken the view that:

In strictly architectural terms, this listed building is almost a complete loss…

The County Planning Officer took a similar initial view (*Ref 7*) which was that:

Any reconstruction of the mill and its machinery above ground floor level would not be valid in terms of listed building conservation because there are no detailed records of what previously existed. In this respect Ron Roper's "full restoration" is out of the question: anything he managed to create would be a modern construction, albeit of a traditional kind, on an authentic ground floor base.

However, the mill did retain its listed status partly on the basis that the machinery that survived the fire was largely intact and partly because of its place in the whole complex of buildings. Mark Barnard summarised the value of the decision:

While it is encouraging that the Secretary of State readily accepted that the working parts of a mill are included in the listing, a local authority must still be able to explain why any machinery under threat is an essential part of the mill, if they are successfully to resist a proposal. In important cases a mill may contain early wooden or cast-iron machinery or millwork by a celebrated engineer, or survive largely unaltered or show a logical sequence of evolution. Other mills may be significant because they show regional variation or are the last intact example in an area.

Finding an *optimum viable use* is challenging but not beyond some creative thinking. In the Stotfold case the inspector said that:

the demand for stone ground flour has improved dramatically the viability of small traditional mills in recent years.

He identified Mapledurham Mill on the Thames as a case in point. The miller there has updated the position on the commercial potential of flour milling. She says that flour production is now limited by the current market. Bakers, who were once the main income source, have been lost to local supermarkets. On the other hand, other trends have been good for the mill, such as farmers' markets, farm shops and a new interest in local shops. Mapledurham Mill now services

The aftermath of the fire at Stotfold showing that although the building was a total loss the hurst frame, machinery and millstones had survived.

Mapledurham Mill. *photo Mildred Cookson*

outlets up to 25 miles away. Grain prices are set to reach all time highs over the next few years because of poor harvests and increased demand from abroad. The price of bread is already reflecting this as flour prices have increased dramatically. Against the income received the costs of paper bags, printing, staff wages and electricity for lighting must be set. In addition there are the soaring costs of maintenance of the building and working parts. Millwrights are few and far between and the cost of materials is high (*Ref 8*).

More locally to Bedfordshire there are a number of mills that are successfully fulfilling a demand for wholemeal flour. Bromham, Ford End and Redbournbury Mills confirm

right: Commercial milling of flour at Mapledurham
photo Luke Bonwick

the point. The inspector in the case of Stotfold considered that revenue from flour production and a throughput of visitors to the mill did enjoy a significant revenue raising capability. Clearly when compared to a straightforward residential conversion, any of these uses will require a creative attitude to producing a viable business plan and putting together attainable funding packages. This is obviously more difficult but it does appear that planning inspectors are taking the view that this is no excuse for not trying. Although the relevant Planning Policy Guidance Note raises the possibility of obtaining funds to support the less economically robust proposals, in practice these are hard to come by. The case of Stoke Mills, Sharnbrook does demonstrate that community uses may be possible. Like the roller mill building at Stotfold the building had lost its plant when the mill was 'silenced' and for 30 years has operated successfully as a theatre.

Similarly a proposal for the use of parts of Barton Mill as a restaurant some years ago received enthusiastic support from molinological interests.

The Mill Theatre, Sharnbrook. *photo Alex Goodbody*

The proposed open plan use will allow the mill and its working parts to be conserved and presented in a much more original state than would dividing up the internal areas for residential or workshop use, for instance. A further advantage of the scheme is that the proposed new use can be achieved with minimal repair and alteration to the original fabric (Ref 9)

The inspector at the Stotfold inquiry crystallised the point about the effect of alternative uses:

It is the impact of the project on the inside of a mill which is cause for most concern. The subdivision of spaces to provide separate rooms would to my mind spoil the existing open appearance of some of the floors, particularly the ground floor and first floor. Machinery, which I consider to be essential to the character of the building, including the drive from the steam engine, shutes, hoppers, and ancillary cleaning and dressing machinery, would be removed or repositioned out of their proper context … Reference was made at the inquiry to the cluttered untidy appearance of the mill machinery floors. This in my experience is an essential characteristic of mill buildings. The conversion to a dwelling, tidying up and drastically altering the interior would to my mind destroy an essential part of the mill's character. It is after all a mill not a dwelling.

There had been arcane debate about the meaning of a building and whether it includes the contents. However, this has been clarified by the decision relating to Stotfold Mill:

Any object or structure fixed to a building should be treated as part of that building. However, it may well be that some objects not actually fixed may yet be included in the listing… (He suggests stone cases, hoppers, horses and a stone crane): items which in the literal sense of the word may not be considered to be fixed.

What is clear is that each case has to be considered on its merits…This may well involve the local planning authority accepting some 'enabling development' which may involve making 'acceptable exceptions' to other planning policies. This need not involve setting undesirable precedents. It may also require the use of planning agreements to ensure that works needed for the conservation of the mill actually take place.

Two windmills in North Bedfordshire offer an instructive contrast in terms of 'enabling development'. The fate of such mills depends very much on whether machinery and equipment is in a restorable condition. In the case of Thurleigh the machinery had largely gone. The ironwork had been removed during the Second World War and little remained that was salvageable. As I wrote in my previous book, *Bedfordshire Mills*, in 1983, 'a sympathetic conversion might be considered an acceptable way of ensuring the retention of this unique Lincolnshire style tower mill.' This indeed is what happened. In 2000 a planning permission was granted and the tower now provides four storeys of living accommodation as part of a new dwelling and includes a viewing area on the top floor with panoramic views of the surrounding countryside. In the case of Upper Dean the local planning authority, in considering an application for the repair and reinstatement of the existing windmill and the construction of a new single dwelling and detached garage, reported that the windmill was sufficiently intact so that it could be conserved. There are very few exceptions to rural restraint policies but the local planning authority took the view that the circumstances were exceptional.

The site lies in open countryside, it is where normal rural restraint policy applies. There are very few exceptions to this policy although it is clear permission can be granted in exceptional circumstances. Each case must be considered on its merits and in this case it has been identified that there are exceptional circumstances in the form of an historic windmill. The mill is on this Council's register of historic buildings at risk. The structure dates from 1856 and is the last remaining example of its type in the county. It has suffered substantial damage and deterioration but the main tower is still in place with two of the sails and most of the machinery intact(although much of it has fallen to the floor). (Ref 10)

The interior of Upper Dean Windmill. Although the mill is now weathertight the collapse of the floors through years of exposure to the elements means that the machinery and millstones are lying where they fell.

The permission was tied into a planning agreement which ensured the repair to the tower and construction of a new cap by specifying that the adjacent new dwelling was not to be occupied before the completion of the restoration works on the windmill itself. The agreement was restricted to making the building weather-tight and did not cover the restoration of the interior, the cost of which would be beyond the scope of the amount of 'enabling development' in question. Full repairs would only be possible on further funds becoming available.

Grange Mill before conversion. *photo J.K. Major*

Conclusion

Since the Secretary of State's decision on Stotfold Mill in 1987 there has been considerable progress in establishing a logical procedure for dealing with planning applications relating to mills. It contrasts with the sad case of Grange Mill, in Heath and Reach. The local planning authority took the view that if the mill was to be restored then an appropriate alternative use had to be found. It seemed that a satisfactory proposal was achieved in 1979 whereby a dwelling was to be created out of part of the mill building whilst retaining the waterwheels and the machinery. The mill was then sold with the benefit of a planning permission for use as a dwelling. The purchaser then embarked on a materially different scheme which resulted not only in the loss of the mechanical items, but also of all of the character and integrity of the building and its surroundings.

Nearly 30 years on, the planning system does now seem to be able to deliver better results for the preservation of our milling heritage. It is certainly encouraging that a planning methodology is emerging, even though it has yet to be enshrined in any official document. Reliance is going to have to be put on the binding force of these few precedent cases. Having spent a working lifetime in the profession of Town and Country Planning, I have noted a certain reluctance amongst planning officers to come to terms with the detail of the economics of development and hence of playing a more proactive role in putting together imaginative packages to enable the conservation of listed buildings to take place. There is little doubt in my mind that the preservation of what remains of our milling heritage will depend on the collective ability of mill owners, local planning authorities and organisations concerned with the preservation of mill buildings to develop economic models and methodologies for putting together imaginative financial packages that will allow remaining unaltered mills to be preserved in their original forms or enable imaginative schemes for their after-use to take place. There is scope for some original research to be done on these practicalities of the preservation of mills.

Occasionally a philanthropically minded owner may be found, as at Doolittle Mill, where the mill has been made wind and weather tight, but this is always likely to be the exception rather than the rule.

References

1 Barnard, M., 1992, 'The Protection of Machinery in Windmills and Watermills', *Contact* (Journal of the Institute of Historic Building Conservation) Issue No 31

2 Dept of National Heritage, 1994, Planning Policy Guidance Note 15, Paragraphs 2.18, 3.5, 3.9 and 3.10

3 Decision letter dated 6th May 1987 from Secretary of State relating to Stotfold Mill

4 Department of Communities and Local Government ref number 100-053-394

5 Bonwick, L., 2008, Report on Flitwick Watermill on behalf of SPAB

6 Howes, H., 2008, *Strategic Planning for Water*, Taylor & Francis, Chapter 7

7 Letter from County Planning Officer dated 14th January 1993 to the MP for Mid Beds

8 Mildred Cookson, Miller at Mapledurham and Editor of Mill News

9 Letter from M. Watts dated 13th February 1995 to applicant's agent

10 Report of Bedford Borough Council